HEALTH AND SOCIAL CARE

ALWAYS LEARNING

PEARSON

Published by Pearson Education Limited, Edinburgh Gate, Harlow, Essex, CM20 2JE.

www.pearsonschoolsandfecolleges.co.uk

Units 1, 2 and 8 © Pearson Education Limited 2012, Units 3, 4, 5 and 7 © Liz Haworth 2012,
Unit 6 © Siân Lavers 2012.
Typeset by Phoenix Photosetting, Chatham, Kent, UK
Original illustrations © Pearson Education Limited 2012
Illustrated by Vicky Woodgate and Phoenix Photosetting
Cover design by Pearson Education Limited and Andrew Magee Design
Front cover photo: Getty Images: Digital Vision
Indexing by Sophia Clapham.

The rights of Andy Ashton, Penelope Garnham, Liz Haworth, Heather Higgins and Siân Lavers to
be identified as authors of this work have been asserted by them in accordance with the Copyright,
Designs and Patents Act 1988.

First published 2012.

16 15 14 13
10 9 8 7 6 5 4 3

British Library Cataloguing in Publication Data
A catalogue record for this book is available from the British Library

ISBN 978 1 446905 62 3

Printed in the UK at Ashford Colour Press, Gosport, Hants

Websites
There are links to relevant websites in this book. In order to ensure that the links are up to date,
that the links works, and that the sites aren't inadvertently links to sites that could be considered
offensive, we have made the links available on our website at www.pearsonhotlinks.co.uk. Search for
the title BTEC First Health and Social Care Award Student Book or ISBN 978 1 446905 62 3.

Copies of official specifications for all Pearson qualifications may be found on the website:
www.edexcel.com

A note from the publisher
In order to ensure that this resource offers high-quality support for the associated BTEC qualification,
it has been through a review process by the awarding organisation to confirm that it fully covers the
teaching and learning content of the specification or part of a specification at which it is aimed, and
demonstrates an appropriate balance between the development of subject skills, knowledge and
understanding, in addition to preparation for assessment.
While the publishers have made every attempt to ensure that advice on the qualification and its
assessment is accurate, the official specification and associated assessment guidance materials are
the only authoritative source of information and should always be referred to for definitive guidance.
No material from an endorsed book will be used verbatim in any assessment set by BTEC.
Endorsement of a book does not mean that the book is required to achieve this BTEC qualification,
nor does it mean that it is the only suitable material available to support the qualification, and
any resource lists produced by the awarding organisation shall include this and other appropriate
resources.

Contents

I'd like to dedicate the four units of this book which I have written to my father, Trevor John Davis, who sadly died at the age of 90 in January 2012. His diverse experiences of health and social care in the last three years of his life, until when he had always been fit and active, and his courageous fight for life at the end, have given me much insight and inspiration. He and Mum have always been very supportive and proud of me and I miss him so much.

Liz Haworth.

Credits

About this book

This qualification will help to prepare you for virtually any career in any sector by equipping you with communication skills, organizational ability, and the ability to present your ideas clearly. Awareness of the stages of human lifespan development and an understanding of health and social care values underpin every role in the wide-ranging health and social care sector, meaning that you will have skills and knowledge that will be valued by employers. In addition, a BTEC First Health and Social Care qualification can help you to progress to the next level of study.

About the authors

Andy Ashton is the Assistant Vice Principal, Curriculum and Academic Standards at Trinity Academy, Doncaster, where he leads the health and social care teaching. He is an author of several books on health and social care, and road safety, and he is actively involved in the coaching of young athletes.

Penelope Garnham has worked as a nurse and midwife for many years prior to entering the field of education. She has taught, lectured, written, verified and trained in schools, FE, HE and the private sector in a great many health-related subjects.

Elizabeth Haworth has taught GCSE Health and Social Care at Lowton High School for over 15 years and has taken a prominent role in LA Steering Groups for developing GCSE and the Diploma. She is the author of several books on Health and Social Care for GCSE, Diploma and BTEC.

Heather Higgins has worked in adults' and children's social services and is a qualified nurse. She taught health and social care in the FE sector for 15 years and is the author of several books on health and social care. Heather was also involved for several years as a volunteer, working with young offenders and latterly with adults who have learning disabilities.

Siân Lavers has 16 years' experience in teaching health and social care in both colleges and universities and is a specialist in health and nutrition education. She is the author of several books on health and social care and is a qualified nurse.

How to use this book

This book contains many features that will help you use your skills and knowledge in work-related situations, and assist you in getting the most from your course.

These introductions give you a snapshot of what to expect from each unit – and what you should be aiming for by the time you finish it.

How this unit is assessed

Learning aims describe what you will be doing in the unit.

A learner shares their experience in relation to the unit.

Features of this book

There are lots of features in this book to help you learn about the topics in each unit, and to have fun while learning! These pages show some of the features that you will come across when using the book.

Topic references show which parts of the BTEC you are covering on these pages.

Getting started with a short activity or discussion about the topic.

Key terms appear in blue bold text and are defined either within the text or in a key term box on the page.

Also see the glossary for definitions of important words and phrases.

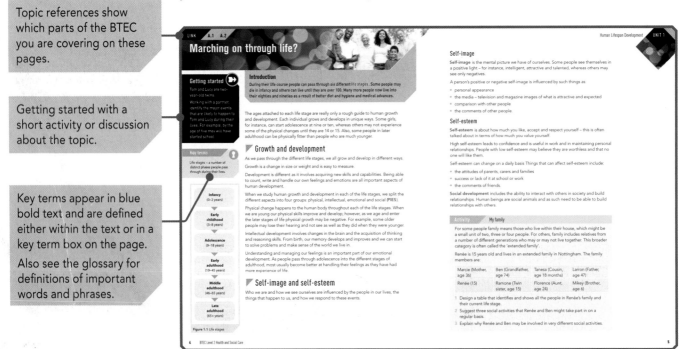

Activity   Learning to share

The process of learning to share with others continues during childhood and adolescence, although some people still find it hard to share even when they are adults.

It is important that parents and carers encourage sharing during infancy and childhood.

1 Identify three play activities that would be ideal for a group of infants or young children that would encourage them to share.

2 Select one of these activities and plan and carry it out with two or three infants.

3 Write up your observations and conclusions.

Activities will help you learn about the topic. These will be done in pairs or groups, or sometimes on your own.

Assessment practice 1.1

Kian is 6 years old. He lives with his mother, baby sister, Ella (9 months old), his grandfather and grandmother.

1 Identify three fine motor skills Kian will have developed by the age of six. (3 marks)

2 Identify three physical skills Kian has mastered that Ella couldn't do in infancy. (3 marks)

3 Explain, using examples, the difference between fine and gross motor skills. (6 marks)

4 Explain why having positive 'role models' is important for children. (4 marks)

A chance to practise answering the types of test questions that you may come across in your exam. (For Unit 1 only.)

Assessment activity 4.2   2B.P3 | 2B.M2 | 2B.D2

As a youth worker at a youth centre in a big town, you have already produced a series of leaflets for the local healthcare centre to help raise awareness of the effects of primary and secondary socialisation on the health and wellbeing of young people.

The staff at the centre ask you to extend your leaflets to produce a report to show parents and their children the influence of different types of relationships, and the positive and negative ways these can influence their health and wellbeing.

Tips

When describing the influence of a range of relationships, which includes the influence of any changes in relationships, you should use evidence such as research from articles in the media or scientific and health-related reports, and give reasons to support the points you are making. Compare the likely negative and positive influences of the person's different relationships on their health and wellbeing.

Activities that relate to the unit's assessment critera. These activities will help you prepare for your assignments and contain tips to help you achieve your potential. (For all units **except** Unit 1.)

Just checking

1 Describe three ways of adapting activities to meet particular needs.

2 Why does providing care that takes account of an individual's likes, dislikes and preferences empower them?

3 Why is it important to be willing to work with other people in health and social care?

Use these to check your knowledge and understanding of the topic you have just covered.

Someone who works in the Health and Social Care industry explains how this unit of the BTEC First applies to the day-to-day work they do as part of their job.

WorkSpace

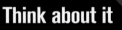

April Forrester
School Nurse

I am a school nurse based in a small town. I work in a team that includes three early years workers, other health professionals and various support staff. We have a base, but I spend most of my time in the various secondary schools to which I am allocated.

My main task is to provide preventative health services to help the learners grow and develop in the best way possible. I identify problems and provide services, such as health education, and referral to other services and care, in order to prevent more serious problems developing later, which would be more difficult to deal with and more costly to address. I work with groups of, and individual, learners. I sometimes speak to a whole year group about an issue, and hold drop-in clinics at schools for any learners to come along and have a private chat with me. Issues they talk to me about are very varied, from unwanted pregnancies to personal hygiene or problems with parents and friends. I have a full range of printed health-promotion materials available, so I can give learners leaflets, which tell them where to find more help if needed. I can also refer them to more specialist agencies that can help them with their specific problems.

I help at school events, such as learning days, when a health input is required, and work with other nurses to carry out year group vaccinations, such as HPV. It is a very satisfying job, because although I speak to many learners when they are upset or worried, it is good to feel that I am helping them, and as no two problems are exactly the same it is a very varied job, so never boring. Sometimes it is very sad, such as when a relative, friend, learner or teacher has died, and learners need to talk through their feelings, but it is often fun, as I really enjoy working with young people.

Think about it

1 Why are communication skills so important to April's job?
2 How does April promote health among young people?
3 How can you make use of health-promotion materials to make sure you keep yourself fit and healthy?

121

This section also gives you the chance to think more about the role that this person does, and whether you would want to follow in their footsteps once you've completed your BTEC.

BTEC Assessment Zone

You will be assessed in two different ways for your BTEC First Health and Social Care Award. For most units, your teacher/tutor will set assignments for you to complete. These may take the form of projects where you research, plan, prepare, and evaluate a piece of work or activity. The table in this BTEC Assessment Zone explains what you must do in order to achieve each of the assessment criteria. Each unit of this book contains a number of assessment activities to help you with these assessment criteria.

The table in the BTEC Assessment Zone explains what you must do in order to achieve each of the assessment criteria, and signposts assessment activities in this book to help you to prepare for your assignments

Assessment criteria		
Level 1	Level 2 Pass	Level 2 Merit
Learning aim A: Explore the core values that underpin current practice in health and social care		
1A.1 English	**2A.P1** English	**2A.M1** English
Identify how care values are used to support users of services.	Describe how care values support users of services, using relevant examples. **Assessment activity 2.1 See page 41.**	Discuss the importance of the values that underpin current practice in health and social care, with reference to selected examples. **Assessment activity 2.1 See page 41.**

Activities in this book will show you the kinds of task you might be asked to do to meet these criteria when your tutor sets an assignment.

Background information

John is 31 years of age and a care assistant in a day centre for older people. He works closely with Betty and Ray, who are both 83 years of age.

Betty and Ray both have problems with walking and mobility. They find completing everyday tasks quite difficult. They have two children and a number of close friends who live very near their home.

'Identify the current life stages of John and Betty'. (2 marks)

This is a very straightforward question. You will need to have learned off by heart the life stages and the ages attached to them to answer this question.

In answering the question you just need to state the life stage for each person and do not need to write in full sentences.

'Give two examples of physical changes which occur in middle adulthood'. (2 marks)

In order to answer this type of question you

'Explain how two different types of informal support could help Betty and Ray with their everyday living'. (4 marks)

In this sort of question hints are often given in the background information which help you in your answers. It is important to go back and look at the information given. Make sure that you look at two different types of informal support and try to make sure you do not repeat yourself in your answer.

You will need to write in full sentences and make sure you link the types of support to how they could help Betty and Ray with everyday living.

'Assess the possible impact attending the day centre may have for Betty and Ray's development'. (8 marks)

There will usually be at least one longer question on the paper where you will be required to write at length about a particular topic or issue.

This type of question will be worth the most marks on the paper and you will need to do a lot of thinking before you write. You are likely to be asked to look at something from a number of different points of view and asked to 'assess' or 'evaluate' the effect of something.

In this particular question you are asked to look at how attending the day centre may affect Betty and

For Unit 1 of your BTEC, you will be assessed by a paper-based exam. The BTEC Assessment Zone in Unit 1 helps you to prepare for your exam by showing you some of the different types of questions you may need to answer.

Study skills

▶ Planning and getting organised

The first step in managing your time is to plan ahead and be well organised. Some people are naturally good at this. They think ahead, write down commitments in a diary or planner and store their notes and handouts neatly and carefully so they can find them quickly.

How good are your working habits?

Improving your planning and organisational skills

1 Use a diary to schedule working times into your weekdays and weekends.

2 Also use the diary to write down exactly what work you have to do. You could use this as a 'to do' list and tick off each task as you go.

3 Divide up long or complex tasks into manageable chunks and put each 'chunk' in your diary with a deadline of its own.

4 Always allow more time than you think you need for a task.

▶ Sources of information

You will need to use research to complete your BTEC First assignments, so it's important to know what sources of information are available to you. These are likely to include the following:

Take it further

If you become distracted by social networking sites or texts when you're working, set yourself a time limit of 10 minutes or so to indulge yourself. You could even use this as a reward for completing a certain amount of work.

Key terms

Bias – People often have strong opinions about certain topics. This is called 'bias'. Newspaper or magazine articles, or information found on the internet, may be biased to present a specific point of view.

Remember!

Store relevant information when you find it – keep a folder on your computer specifically for research – so you don't have to worry about finding it again at a later date.

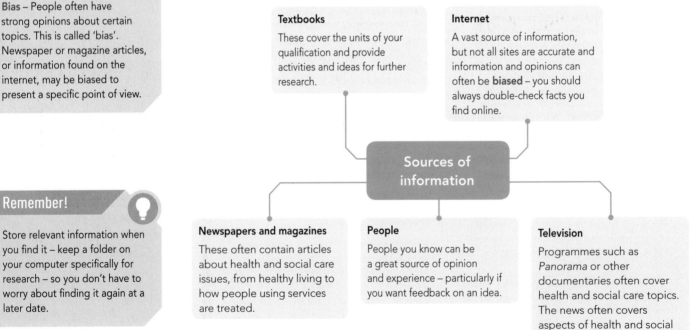

Textbooks
These cover the units of your qualification and provide activities and ideas for further research.

Internet
A vast source of information, but not all sites are accurate and information and opinions can often be **biased** – you should always double-check facts you find online.

Sources of information

Newspapers and magazines
These often contain articles about health and social care issues, from healthy living to how people using services are treated.

People
People you know can be a great source of opinion and experience – particularly if you want feedback on an idea.

Television
Programmes such as *Panorama* or other documentaries often cover health and social care topics. The news often covers aspects of health and social care such as the NHS.

Organising and selecting information

Organising your information

Once you have used a range of sources of information for research, you will need to organise the information so it's easy to use.

- Make sure your written notes are neat and have a clear heading – it's often useful to date them, too.
- Always keep a note of where the information came from (the title of a book, the title and date of a newspaper or magazine and the web address of a website) and, if relevant, which pages.
- Work out the results of any questionnaires you've used.

Selecting your information

Once you have completed your research, re-read the assignment brief or instructions you were given to remind yourself of the exact wording of the question(s) and divide your information into three groups:

1 Information that is totally relevant.
2 Information that is not as good, but which could come in useful.
3 Information that doesn't match the questions or assignment brief very much, but that you kept because you couldn't find anything better!

Check that there are no obvious gaps in your information against the questions or assignment brief. If there are, make a note of them so that you know exactly what you still have to find.

Presenting your work

Before handing in any assignments, make sure:

- you have addressed each part of the question and that your work is as complete as possible
- all spelling and grammar is correct
- you have referenced all sources of information you used for your research
- all work is your own – otherwise you could be committing **plagiarism**
- you have saved a copy of your work.

Key terms

Plagiarism – If you are including other people's views, comments or opinions, or copying a diagram or table from another publication, you must state the source by including the name of the author or publication, or the web address. Failure to do this (when you are really pretending other people's work is your own) is known as plagiarism. Check your school's policy on plagiarism and copying.

Introduction

Human growth and development is a topic that affects us all. Health and social care professionals need to have a detailed understanding of these changes.

In this unit you will explore how people grow and develop throughout their lives and the factors that affect this growth and development. To make it easier to understand these changes we have split human development into four areas: physical, intellectual, emotional and social.

You will investigate the factors that influence change and development, such as our genes, our environment and the people we choose to have relationships with. You will see how life choices and events affect how we grow and develop.

This unit will help you gain a clear understanding of the support available to manage the changes caused by life events.

Assessment: You will be assessed by a paper-based examination lasting one hour.

Learning aims

In this unit you will:

A explore human growth and development across life stages

B investigate factors that affect human growth and development and how they are interrelated.

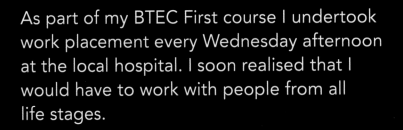

As part of my BTEC First course I undertook work placement every Wednesday afternoon at the local hospital. I soon realised that I would have to work with people from all life stages.

John, *would-be nurse, aged 17 years.*

Human Lifespan Development

1

Marching on through life?

Getting started ▶▶

Tom and Lucy are two-year-old twins.

Working with a partner, identify the major events that are likely to happen to Tom and Lucy during their lives. For example, by the age of five they will have started school.

Introduction

During their life course people can pass through six different life stages. Some people may die in infancy and others can live until they are over 100. Many more people now live into their eighties and nineties as a result of better diet and hygiene and medical advances.

The ages attached to each life stage are really only a rough guide to human growth and development. Each individual grows and develops in unique ways. Some girls, for instance, can start adolescence at nine or ten, whereas others may not experience some of the physical changes until they are 14 or 15. Also, some people in later adulthood can be physically fitter than people who are much younger.

Key terms

Life stages – a number of distinct phases people pass through during their lives.

Growth and development

As we pass through the different life stages, we all grow and develop in different ways.

Growth is a change in size or weight and is easy to measure.

Development is different as it involves acquiring new skills and capabilities. Being able to count, write and handle our own feelings and emotions are all important aspects of human development.

When we study human growth and development in each of the life stages, we split the different aspects into four groups: physical, intellectual, emotional and social (**PIES**).

Physical change happens to the human body throughout each of the life stages. When we are young our physical skills improve and develop; however, as we age and enter the later stages of life physical growth may be negative. For example, some older people may lose their hearing and not see as well as they did when they were younger.

Intellectual development involves changes in the brain and the acquisition of thinking and reasoning skills. From birth, our memory develops and improves and we can start to solve problems and make sense of the world we live in.

Understanding and managing our feelings is an important part of our emotional development. As people pass through adolescence into the different stages of adulthood, most usually become better at handling their feelings as they have had more experience of life.

Self-image and self-esteem

Who we are and how we see ourselves are influenced by the people in our lives, the things that happen to us, and how we respond to these events.

Infancy
(0–2 years)

▼

Early childhood
(3–8 years)

▼

Adolescence
(9–18 years)

▼

Early adulthood
(19–45 years)

▼

Middle adulthood
(46–65 years)

▼

Late adulthood
(65+ years)

Figure 1.1 Life stages

Self-image

Self-image is the mental picture we have of ourselves. Some people see themselves in a positive light – for instance, intelligent, attractive and talented, whereas others may see only negatives.

A person's positive or negative self-image is influenced by such things as:

- personal appearance
- the media – television and magazine images of what is attractive and expected
- comparison with other people
- the comments of other people.

Self-esteem

Self-esteem is about how much you like, accept and respect yourself – this is often talked about in terms of how much you value yourself.

High self-esteem leads to confidence and is useful in work and in maintaining personal relationships. People with low self-esteem may believe they are worthless and that no one will like them.

Self-esteem can change on a daily basis. Things that can affect self-esteem include:

- the attitudes of parents, carers and families
- success or lack of it at school or work
- the comments of friends.

Social development includes the ability to interact with others in society and build relationships. Human beings are social animals and as such need to be able to build relationships with others.

Activity	My family

For some people family means those who live within their house, which might be a small unit of two, three or four people. For others, family includes relatives from a number of different generations who may or may not live together. This broader category is often called the 'extended family'.

Renée is 15 years old and lives in an extended family in Nottingham. The family members are:

Marcie (Mother, age 36)	Ben (Grandfather, age 74)	Tanesa (Cousin, age 18 months)	Larron (Father, age 47)
Renée (15)	Ramone (Twin sister, age 15)	Florence (Aunt, age 24)	Mikey (Brother, age 6)

1 Design a table that identifies and shows all the people in Renée's family and their current life stage.

2 Suggest three social activities that Renée and Ben might take part in on a regular basis.

3 Explain why Renée and Ben may be involved in very different social activities.

Starting out

Getting started ⏩

Working in a small group, discuss and then make a list of the major skills infants are likely to have mastered by the age of two. For example, nearly all infants will be able to walk.

Infancy (0–2)

From being born weighing just a few kilos to reaching the age of two, an infant grows and develops in many ways. In fact, infancy is the time when growth and development are at their most rapid.

Physical development

The physical changes that happen in infancy can be split into **gross motor skill** and **fine motor skill** development. Gross motor skills mean that the infant can start to control the larger muscles of the body; fine motor skills mean that it can control the smaller muscles. Examples of each would be starting to walk and holding a spoon. These skills improve and develop greatly in early childhood.

Key terms 🔑

Gross motor skill – the ability to control and coordinate the movement of the large limbs of the body, e.g. crawling, walking and running.

Fine motor skill – the ability to control and coordinate the movements of the hands and fingers, e.g. writing, painting, tying shoelaces and holding a spoon.

Language development – the process which children go through as they learn to communicate with others using words and speech.

Egocentric – seeing things from only your own perspective or viewpoint.

Bond – to form an attachment with a parent/carer.

Table 1.1 Muscle control

Muscle control	Approximate age
Can grasp objects with whole hand	4 months
Can start to crawl	8 months
Can climb stairs and run – but often falls	18 months
Can control large muscles, which allows for toilet training	2 years

Infancy is a major developmental stage.

Intellectual development

Intellectual development is about thinking and the way the mind works. At birth babies respond to the world through their senses and communicate mainly through sound. Smiles and noises become the main way of communicating with carers. If infants are hungry they cry. Words do not usually form part of communication until around the age of one year. Before learning to use words, infants babble a lot to express their feelings. By 18 months most infants will know about six words and by two years most will be able to put two to three words together into a simple sentence. **Language development** is a major intellectual change during infancy. During infancy a baby experiences the world through its senses and can only see the world from their own viewpoint. This is known as being **egocentric**.

Emotional development

During the first two years of life infants **bond** with those who care for them. Up to about six months babies do not mind who holds them, though they may not like being put down. Between 7 and 12 months infants form a strong bond with their main carers and will be very wary of strangers and often cry if held by others. From about 12 months infants are able to start to form bonds with other people. This is known as the attachment process. It is important that infants receive love and affection during the attachment process as this influences emotional development throughout future life stages.

Social development

Early relationship development in infancy is based on interaction with others and this shapes social development. These relationships also act as a model for future relationships. The main relationships in infancy are those with parents, carers and brothers and sisters.

A great deal of social learning comes through play. In early infancy children play alone but as they grow older they begin to play first alongside others, and eventually with others, and start to learn about the process of sharing.

Activity	Learning to share

The process of learning to share with others continues during childhood and adolescence, although some people still find it hard to share even when they are adults.

It is important that parents and carers encourage sharing during infancy and childhood.

1 Identify three play activities that would be ideal for a group of infants or young children that would encourage them to share.

2 Select one of these activities and plan and carry it out with two or three infants.

3 Write up your observations and conclusions.

Bigger and better?

Getting started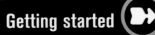

In a small group, think back to when you were six or seven. What sort of games did you play?

How did these games help promote the development of the PIES stages?

In what ways are the games girls play different from those that boys play?

Introduction

All children love to play, and in early childhood play is important for development.

Early childhood (3–8)

Early childhood is an exciting time for growth and development as infants become more independent from their carers and begin to make more sense of the world and their place in it. Children love to learn and develop new skills at this age.

Physical development

The development of gross and fine motor skills improves greatly during childhood. From only being able to do a limited range of activities with support in early infancy, by the age of eight most children can do many activities independently. At five, children can walk upstairs unaided and hold a crayon or pencil to draw and write. By eight, children can usually catch and throw quite well and will have a good sense of balance. Many top-class tennis players, for example, were already very good at the game by this age, having already developed good hand–eye coordination.

Intellectual development

By the end of early childhood children have progressed greatly in their intellectual development. Most children are able to speak in full sentences and have quite a good vocabulary. Children also start school during this stage of their life, and this helps with development of language and understanding of numbers.

In infancy, the world is experienced through the senses alone. In childhood this changes as children have the ability to be able to think about things that happen to them. However, they still tend to be egocentric, seeing the world from only their own viewpoint.

Children learn how to act and behave in particular situations by watching others and asking questions. For example, children have to be taught how to behave and eat at the dining table. As children see how their carers respond in particular situations, they begin to copy this behaviour. This is why it is important that children have positive role models in their lives.

Children can learn both how to behave at the dining table and about healthy eating from role models such as their parents.

Emotional development

Between the ages of three and eight children will begin to learn how to handle their feelings. They learn how to share and cooperate with other people. Children can tell others when they feel happy or sad and begin to explain their feelings. It is also during this period that children begin to develop their own self-concept, which will be further developed throughout life.

Social development

Between three and eight years of age children begin to widen their social group and form friendships with others. In the early part of this life stage children often have temper tantrums if they cannot have their own way. Gradually they begin to realise that they have to cooperate with others. By the age of eight, children will usually have a number of friends and often have what they call a 'best friend'.

There are different stages that children go through as they learn to play.

Table 1.2 Children's play stages

Type of play	Age	Description of play
Solitary play (Infancy)	0–2 years	Children play alone using their imagination and do not interact with other children.
Parallel play	2–3 years	Children play alongside each other, but not together. Toys are not shared cooperatively.
Social play	3–8 years	Children play together, sharing their toys. By the age of eight they will engage in quite complex games, often requiring the use of imagination.

Assessment practice 1.1

Kian is 6 years old. He lives with his mother, baby sister, Ella (9 months old), his grandfather and grandmother.

1 Identify three fine motor skills Kian will have developed by the age of six. (3 marks)

2 Identify three physical skills Kian has mastered that Ella couldn't do in infancy. (3 marks)

3 Explain, using examples, the difference between fine and gross motor skills. (6 marks)

4 Explain why having positive 'role models' is important for children. (4 marks)

It is really important to make sure that you answer the questions set. For questions that ask you to 'identify' a list will be good enough to get the marks.

For 'Explain' questions you will need to write in more depth, using sentences and paragraphs, for these answers.

Always make sure you do exactly what the question asks. If you are asked to give examples, for instance, these are required to get the marks, so don't miss them out.

Teenage years

Introduction

Adolescence is a time of great physical and emotional change.

Adolescence (9–18)

Adolescence is a stage of great physical, intellectual, emotional and social change. Children entering adolescence pass through puberty and become adults. One of the key physical features of puberty is the reaching of sexual maturity. People enter adolescence at different ages, with girls on average entering adolescence slightly earlier than boys. But everyone is different and the normal age range for entering puberty is quite wide. For instance, although on average most girls start menstruation between the ages of 12 and 13, the normal range is anything from eight to 16.

Physical development

In adolescence there is a rapid process of physical change caused as a result of hormonal change. The physical changes in girls are caused by **oestrogen**, and those in boys are caused by **testosterone**.

Intellectual development

One of the biggest intellectual changes that happens in adolescence is the development of **abstract thinking**. This is the ability to think using concepts and ideas rather than through using objects and doing tasks. A seven-year-old child may be able to calculate how long it takes to travel to a destination by train through pushing the fingers of a clock round its face, whereas teenagers can usually do this calculation in their heads.

Adolescents also begin to think in a more logical way to solve problems and can **empathise** – see things from other people's perspective and realise that the world is not centred totally round them. This period is also a time when teenagers develop their own set of morals and ideas about what is right and wrong.

Have you had to comfort a friend?

Emotional development

The large hormonal changes in the body mean that adolescence can be a difficult time for teenagers. Mood swings, frustrations, insecurities and confusions are all common and most teenagers experience them. It is at this time that young people begin to form their own personality and identity.

Feelings of physical attraction towards others also begin to develop during adolescence. Young people start to explore their own sexuality, usually with the opposite sex, but sometimes with the same sex. It is during adolescence that many young people have their first close and intimate relationship with another person. Relationships are formed and sometimes maintained for quite long periods of time. However, many are short-lived and the teenager has to handle a whole new range of feelings and emotions to do with loss and grief.

Social development

Social development in teenagers is closely linked to their emotional development. It is during adolescence that young people tend to socialise more and have more independence and freedom. Young people are also influenced greatly by the views, opinions and behaviour of their close friends. This is known as **peer group** pressure.

Peer group pressure is a challenge for all teenagers and their families. It often causes conflict, as the views of teenagers may be very different from the views of their parents. The close friendships formed in adolescence may well last well into adulthood and many people maintain these friendships throughout their whole life.

Discussion point

Many teenagers feel that they can make their own decisions. This independence can cause conflict with parents/carers. In pairs, discuss the following statements. Do you agree?

- 17 is old enough for someone to decide what time they come home.
- It is acceptable for teenagers to receive family planning advice and treatment without their parents'/carers' knowledge or consent.

Why is it difficult to remain unaffected by peer pressure?

Being independent

Getting started

Working in a small group, discuss how and why the social life of a person who is 22 may be very different from a person who is 42. Be prepared to share your views with the group.

Introduction

Early adulthood is the time when many young people have an active social life and a wide network of friends.

Early adulthood (19–45)

Early adulthood is a time when people reach their physical peak and become mature. Common features of this period include starting work, meeting a partner, settling down and starting a family. It is an exciting time for most people as they grow and develop in different ways.

Physical development

Most people reach their physical peak in the first part of early adulthood. This is when they are physically at their strongest. Top sprinters, for example, are usually at their best when they are in their mid-twenties. However, with training and good levels of motivation, athletes can continue to perform at the top level well into their thirties.

Early adulthood is the time when many people find partners, marry and have children.

Towards the end of this life stage physical capabilities start to diminish and fertility levels also begin to fall. Some women will to go through the **menopause** in early adulthood and the live sperm count of men also begins to fall. As people's metabolic rates slow down they also begin to burn fewer calories and as a result some people will put on weight. However, gaining weight can be countered through a careful diet and regular exercise. People who exercise regularly and take care of their diet often look much younger than their biological age.

Intellectual development

Nearly all people have the capability for intellectual development throughout adulthood. Many people who did not focus fully on learning at school often decide to carry on their education in their twenties or thirties. Many people develop in their careers and need to gain new skills and better qualifications to improve their career prospects. 'Lifelong learning' is now accepted as being important for all people and intellectual capability is often improved in early adulthood.

Emotional development

Early adulthood is the time that many people develop close and intimate relationships with others. Some people cohabit, some choose to marry or, if a same-sex couple, have a civil partnership ceremony. Intimate relationships create feelings of security and allow people to give and receive love. Some people may choose to live alone and others live alone as a result of relationship breakdown.

Early adulthood is also the time when most people choose to start a family. Having children often gives people a sense of direction in life and they enjoy forming close emotional bonds with their children. Time spent with children also gives parents a lot of pleasure as they watch their children take their first steps and speak their first words. But parenthood comes with responsibilities and not all couples choose to have children.

Social development

During the early years of young adulthood, people are generally free to have a very active social life, making new friends and building new relationships. As people move through early adulthood they usually gain more responsibilities. By 45, for instance, many people will be married, and have children, a responsible job and a mortgage to pay. Balancing work life, family life and a social life can be very difficult for people as their responsibilities increase.

Key terms

Menopause – the natural and permanent stopping of menstruation (periods), occurring usually between the ages of 45 and 55.

Discussion point

John and Mike have been together for four years and have recently been through a civil ceremony and consider themselves married. They want to start a family and Mike's friend from college has agreed to be a surrogate mother.

1 Explain how starting a family may affect John and Mike's social life.

2 Discuss the benefits of having children for John and Mike's emotional development.

3 How might John and Mike's relationship be affected by having a family of their own?

4 Do you think John and Mike's life as parents would be any different from a heterosexual couple starting a family?

Halfway through?

Getting started ⏩

Working with a partner, draw up two lists for:

- the benefits of being in middle adulthood
- the possible negatives of being in middle adulthood.

Be prepared to share your ideas with the group.

Key terms 🔑

Mid-life crisis – a dramatic period of self-doubt caused by the passing of youth and the move into later adulthood.

Introduction

As people enter middle adulthood they begin to realise that they are no longer young.

Middle adulthood (46–65)

Middle adulthood is a time when many major physical and emotional changes take place in people's lives. As they reach the age of 50 or 60 people begin to realise that they are getting older but still feel young inside. This can lead to some people having a **mid-life crisis**.

Physical development

As people move through middle adulthood the ageing process begins to take effect in the human body. Physical capabilities start to decline and muscle tone isn't as good as it was. People often feel they have lower energy levels than in early adulthood, and sight and hearing may start to decline. As the skin begins to lose its elasticity wrinkles often become more noticeable. Hair becomes greyer and some men lose more of their hair and may become bald.

It is during this life stage that most women go through the menopause. This usually happens between the ages of 45 and 55. Women produce less oestrogen and the menstrual cycle eventually stops for most women by the end of this life stage. Men also produce less testosterone and live sperm production decreases.

Intellectual development

Intellectual development continues throughout middle adulthood and many people choose to return to education and study. This sometimes happens by choice as some people want a new direction in life, but for others it may be sparked through the need to get new qualifications. Most people will have a variety of jobs throughout their working lives and therefore need retraining.

As we age, our memories might not be as quick as they once were, but older people have a lot of life experience.

Getting older doesn't have to slow you down.

Emotional development

During middle adulthood hormone changes take place in the body which can be linked to changing feelings and emotions.

This leads many people to review their lives at this stage. Some try to recapture their youth through behaving in ways similar to those in early adulthood. They may dress younger than their years and start going out more. They may wish to try things they have never done before. This sort of behaviour has led to the use of the phrase 'mid-life crisis'.

These sorts of feelings are quite normal and may last for a number of years until people come to terms with who they are.

Activity	Empty nest syndrome

With a partner explore what is meant by the term 'empty nest syndrome'.

Social development

As children may have left the family home and become independent, middle-aged people often have more time on their hands and have more money to spend than ever before. This provides an opportunity for some people to extend their social lives. Middle-aged people may start to build new relationships, travel more and just have more quality time to spend with their family. However, in more difficult financial times, with high unemployment and limited job opportunities, many middle-aged people may find themselves out of work or having to support their adult children financially and help with child support for grandchildren.

Assessment practice 1.2

Jozef (59) and Kamilla (55) have been married for 30 years. Their youngest child Beata (21) left home last year and lives nearby with her boyfriend and their baby.

1 Identify three features that indicate that people are ageing. (3 marks)
2 Explain what is meant by the term 'mid-life crisis'. (4 marks)
3 Explain why middle adulthood may be a time of opportunity for Jozef and Kamilla. (4 marks)
4 In what ways are the social lives of Jozef and Kamilla different from Beata's social life? (6 marks)

Remember to work on your examination technique in your practice answers.

You will be asked to remember key facts that you have learned – questions for this will normally have 1 mark for each answer.

Questions may ask, for example, 'identify', 'give', 'define' or 'select' (from a list).

'Explain' means the examiner needs some depth in the answer.

Remember you need to do what the question asks.

Ensure answers are written in full sentences and make sure the answer makes sense.

Re-read your answers at the end of the examination to make sure that you have not misunderstood the question and that you have completed all parts of the question.

Times of change

Introduction

Puzzles, quizzes, crosswords and sudoku are all popular with some people in later adulthood.

Later adulthood (65+)

In later adulthood people often find they have more time on their hands. Improvements in diet and medical treatment mean many people can expect to live 20 to 30 more years after they retire from work at 65. In fact more people are now choosing to work until they are 70 and some even beyond this age. Older people can be some of the most productive members of society, with skills younger people often wish they had.

Physical development

The ageing process in later adulthood is very clear to see. The skin is thinner, joints are stiffer, muscles weaker and bones often more brittle. Older people are frequently less mobile than younger people and some begin to stoop and lose height. Physical development in this life stage can involve the loss of skills and physical capacities.

Although these changes may seem negative, people in later adulthood can still be very active. Many older people take regular exercise as they have more time than when they were working. This might be through joining gyms, taking exercise classes, walking, running or jogging. Older people appreciate the benefits of regular exercise in keeping mobile and supple.

Fauja Singh is believed to have set the world record for a 100-year-old in the London Marathon in October 2011. He completed the course in 8 hours, 25 minutes and 16 seconds. Most people of any age would find it hard to match this time if they ran a marathon.

Keeping fit in later life is just as important as when we are younger.

Intellectual development

Although speed of thinking and short-term memory might decline in later adulthood, it is thought that intelligence does not change with age. Many older people are keen to learn new things, develop their knowledge and keep their minds active. As older people have more leisure time they may take up new interests, such as learning a different language, gaining new experiences through travel and learning new skills.

Some older people may experience **dementia** as they age and it is more common now as more people live longer on average.

Emotional development

Later adulthood offers the opportunity to spend more quality time with family and friends. Older people often enjoy seeing their children and grandchildren and spending time with them. Instead of rushing and fitting people in around work commitments, retired people can take things at a steadier pace. More time can be spent with people and closer friendships and relationships developed. This often leads to feelings of contentment and happiness.

However, later adulthood can also be a challenge for many people. It is during this stage that people often lose their life partner and friends as they die. Some of these relationships will have existed throughout the person's whole life. This can be distressing and hard to cope with. The support of family, other friends and neighbours can be really important at this stage to make sure the person does not feel isolated and lonely.

Social development

Later adulthood is often split into two parts. The first stage is 65 to 75 and the second stage 75 plus. During the first stage people still tend to be very active and often have a busy social life. They are often 'on the go' and say they don't know how they managed to fit work in when they were younger. As people age beyond 75 they tend to slow down, but this doesn't mean they socialise any less. It just means the type of social life they have may be different.

> **Key terms**
>
> Dementia – an illness that affects the brain and memory, and makes you gradually lose the ability to think and behave normally.

Case study

Liz is 75 years old and is coming to terms with the death of her husband six months ago. They had been happily married for 54 years.

1 Describe two ways in which Liz's children could support her at this difficult time.

2 How might a doctor or counsellor help Liz?

3 Suggest some possible activities Liz could take up to help her meet new people.

Born this way?

Getting started

Tom and John were both talented footballers at junior school and both equally good. They took turns as goalkeeper for the school team. Tom moved to Manchester with his parents at the age of 12 and the boys lost touch.

Nine years later John was watching a premier league football match on television and was surprised to see Tom in goal!

What sort of factors might have helped Tom develop into a premier football league goalkeeper?

Activity

Working in a small group, identify different physical features that are inherited from our parents.

How does ability in childhood translate into success in adulthood?

The influences on human growth and development

How people grow and develop depends on the genes they inherit from their parents and the events and factors that influence them as they age.

The influence of physical factors

With the exception of identical twins, we each have a unique set of genes. Children inherit physical features from their parents. If both parents are tall, for example, there is a much greater chance that their children will also be tall.

Skills and talents can also be passed from parents to children through genes. Talented athletes and sportspeople who marry other top athletes are much more likely to have children who have the same natural talents as well. Some people also argue that other aspects of human nature such as intelligence, personality and sexuality are also linked to our genes.

Some people inherit adverse genetic conditions, which they live with throughout their lives. Down's syndrome is one example. As we age, degenerative diseases also develop as our bodies cope with everyday life. These factors will certainly affect how a person grows and develops across the different life stages.

The choices we make in life regarding diet, exercise, alcohol, smoking and drug use will also affect growth and development. If, for example, a person is heavily overweight this can affect their joints as they become older, and increase the risk of diabetes and heart disease. Type 2 diabetes and high blood pressure are often caused through the type of lifestyle choices we make.

Many people make really positive choices in life, which have a big impact on growth and development. Developing a wide network of friends can have a positive effect on a person's emotional and social wellbeing. Having people to turn to and share problems with is really important when we face unexpected life events such as serious illness, stress or coping with the death of a close family member.

Activity   Everyday choices and their long-term consequences

Working in pairs, look at the possible negative effects of one of the following on growth and development:

- binge drinking
- smoking
- regular eating of fast foods
- running five miles every day
- taking recreational drugs at weekends.

The influence of environmental factors

Although inherited genes do influence growth and development, a whole range of other factors, often known as 'environmental' factors, influence how we grow and develop. For example, a person who has a serious car accident and has to be off school for six months is unlikely to do as well at school as someone who is fully healthy.

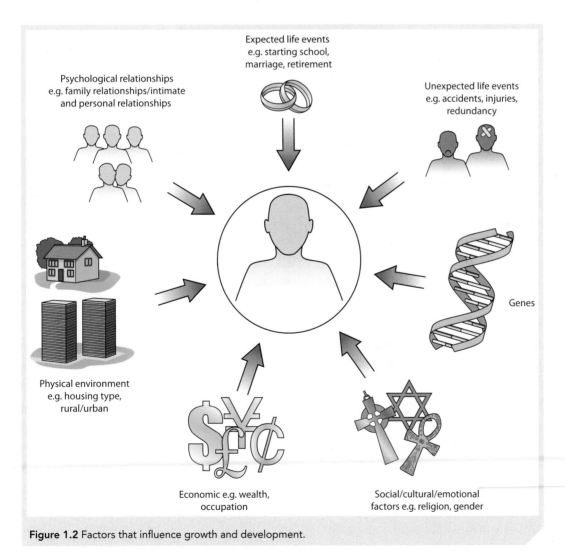

Figure 1.2 Factors that influence growth and development.

Social, cultural and emotional factors

Introduction

Growth and development are influenced throughout the life course by many different social, cultural and emotional factors. Some factors are more important in particular life stages than they are in others.

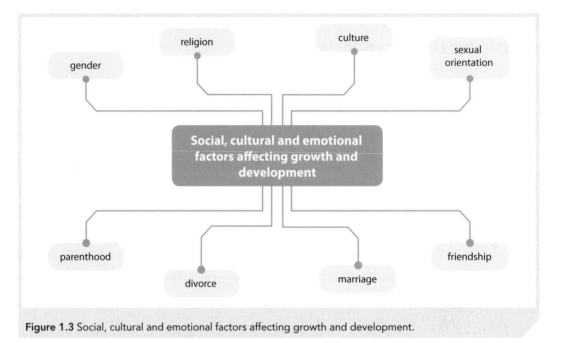

Figure 1.3 Social, cultural and emotional factors affecting growth and development.

Play in infancy and childhood

During the first year of life the infant will begin to play alone. This is known as solitary play.

By the age of two most children are involved in parallel play alongside other children, and they later move on to social play, which involves playing with others. This is sometimes called cooperative play, as children learn to share, use their imagination and get involved in role play. Children love to dress up and learn about the different jobs people have in the world. At this time children are learning the important skills of how to build relationships with others and how to behave as a friend.

What type of play can you identify in this photo?

Activity	Play! Play! Play!

Working in small groups, select four games which children often play together.

For each game identify the skills which the children are likely to be developing.

Remember to use all aspects of the PIES stages in your thinking.

Role models

As people grow and develop they are influenced by the people they interact with in their everyday lives. These people act as **role models** to children and adolescents, who look up to them and often copy their behaviour patterns. Many boys, for example, look up to sports stars such as footballers or rugby players, and many girls want to be like pop stars and models. Children as young as eight will copy the behaviour shown by others.

It is important that young people have good role models in their lives who demonstrate behaviour which has a positive effect on others and society as a whole.

Activity   Role models

Working with a partner, identify two positive and two negative ways in which the following may be role models to young people:

- celebrities
- parents
- school teachers.

A person's **gender role** is also learned from the people they interact with. In the past there were very separate gender roles for men and women. Men went out to work and women stayed at home and were involved in looking after and raising the children. This has now changed hugely and both men and women go out to work and share the caring roles for their children. This means that men are said to have become more in touch with their nurturing side and it is much more acceptable for women to want to follow and develop a career. As a result, we now have much more social equality between men and women and more equality of opportunity in the world of work.

Culture

How people develop is influenced by the community they live in and the values and beliefs which their family and friends hold. Religion can influence how people choose to lead their lives, the food they eat and how they choose to dress. Some people live in communities which hold traditional values about marriage and family roles, while others may live in communities with very different beliefs and values. For example, a Muslim woman may find being examined by a male doctor or nurse traumatic because strict Muslims forbid any physical contact between males and females unless they are married.

It is important that people feel accepted as part of their family and community. Being involved with others makes people feel wanted and valued. This helps people have good self-esteem and promotes growth and development. Unfortunately, some people feel socially isolated from their families and have few friends. This can have a negative impact on growth and development.

Activity   Taking part

In later adulthood many people live by themselves because of the death of their life partner.

Working with a partner, research the types of social groups and activities which are available in your local community which may offer opportunities for older people to meet others and socialise.

Key terms

Role model – someone whose behaviour and/or attitudes people try to copy because they admire them.

Gender role – a role that is determined by a person's gender.

Link

This topic links to Unit 7: Equality and Diversity in Health and Social Care.

Influences on life

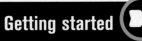

Key terms

Manual work – work that requires the use of physical skills.

Non-manual work – work that depends primarily on mental skills.

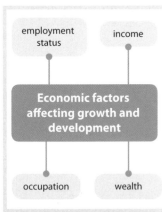

Figure 1.4 Economic factors that affect human growth and development.

Introduction

Getting their first full-time job with regular pay will affect a young person's physical, intellectual, emotional and social development.

◤ Economic factors

How people grow and develop is also influenced greatly by the work they do and how much money they earn. People whose jobs involve **manual work** are often more affected physically by their work than people who do a **non-manual** job such as a desk job. Non-manual and professional jobs also tend to be more highly paid than manual jobs.

Being employed provides workers with an income, allowing them to buy the things they need for themselves and for their families. Work can lead to feelings of contentment and worth and raise self-esteem. Conversely, being unemployed and living on a limited income can lead to feelings of stress and anxiety and a lowering of self-esteem. Some people inherit wealth, which gives them the possibility of a lifestyle very different from that of people who have limited income.

Assessment practice 1.3

Anthony is 22 and works as a manual labourer for a local building company. He works outside all day moving heavy loads and helping the skilled trades people. He earns the minimum wage and lives at home with his parents and two younger brothers.

1 Explain two effects on health and wellbeing of living on a limited income. (4 marks)

2 Explain two possible effects of being employed in manual work on physical health. (4 marks)

You will need to think hard before you write and also make sure you answer the question.

Always write in full sentences and remember to use capital letters and full stops.

Remember to work on your examination technique in your practice answers.

You may be asked to apply your knowledge to a particular situation. Remember that 'explain' means the examiner needs some depth in the answer. Re-read your answers at the end of the examination to make sure you have not misunderstood the question and have completed all parts of the question.

Physical environment factors

Where you live and work can have a major effect on your development, health and wellbeing. City centres can be noisy and crowded with many more health risks. Crime rates tend to be higher and there is often more air and noise pollution. Air pollution has been linked to increases in illnesses, such as asthma. Having space, warmth and a clean home environment all have a positive effect on growth and development. Living in rural areas often provides families with more green space so children can play outside more and have more freedom. Housing can often be cheaper in rural areas, but a disadvantage is that there is often less work available. Rural occupations are often low-paid.

Young people can be attracted to the social opportunities that city life provides, but many people choose to move out of the city when they decide to start a family.

Psychological factors

People have a whole range of different relationships in their lives. These can be split into three main types:

- those with family members
- friendships
- personal and intimate relationships with partners.

Having positive relationships with other people is really important. There are times in life when we will all need the support of our family and friends to help us deal with the problems we face.

If a person is having difficulties with members of their family or friends this might have an effect on how they grow and develop. For example, some children grow up in care and this can sometimes have a negative effect on their self-esteem as they think they are different from other children.

As people progress through different stages in life they may experience stress from life events and this can affect all aspects of growth and development. High levels of stress at work can lead to high blood pressure and increase the risk of heart attacks and strokes.

In the early life stages the family is crucially important as infants and children depend on their parents to meet nearly all their needs. Parents give their children security and accept them as they are. This is known as unconditional acceptance.

As children move into adolescence they begin to be influenced more by their friends and the views and opinions they have. It is also in adolescence that many young people develop their first close and intimate relationships with other people.

Relationships are important for growth and development, and having positive relationships with others leads to the development of a good self-image and high self-esteem. Having a good network of close friends can lead to a sense of happiness and contentment. Most people also enjoy spending time with others and taking part in social activities. However, on some occasions friends can cause distress to others through their actions.

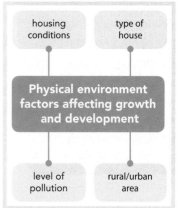

Figure 1.5 Physical environment factors that affect human growth and development.

Discussion point

In small groups, discuss the possible help and support friends might be able to offer a young person who has just had an argument with their best friend.

Life events

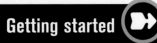

Introduction

Having a supportive family and friends is important for everyone.

As we pass through life we face a whole range of events that will affect aspects of our growth and development. For example, moving to a new house in a different part of the country will be a challenge for all members of a family. Children will have to make new friends and will probably miss the friends they used to see every day. Starting a new school could affect a young person's intellectual development as well. A teenager who moves to a new school part of the way through Year 10 might not be able to complete the course they were doing in their previous school, which could affect their examination results at 16 and influence them for the rest of their life.

Expected life events

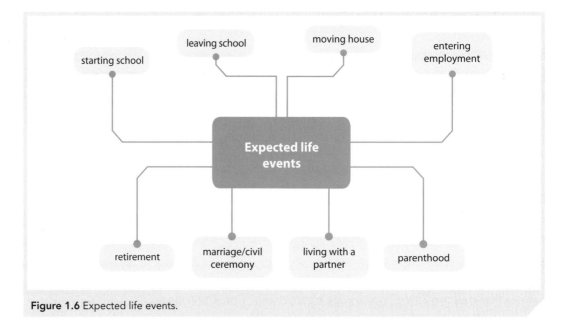

Figure 1.6 Expected life events.

It is important to remember that some life events are expected and predictable, and can therefore be planned for and managed.

Activity	The effect of expected life events

In small groups, consider how the physical, intellectual, emotional and social development of a person might be affected by each of the following expected life events:

- starting or leaving school
- getting a full-time job
- moving in with a partner
- retiring from work.

Unexpected life events

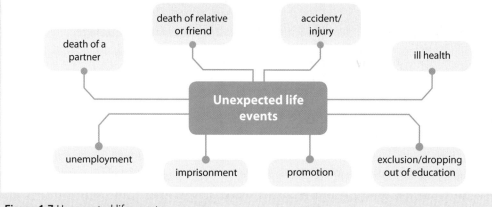

Figure 1.7 Unexpected life events.

Unfortunately, life does not always go to plan and unexpected life events will happen. For example, if a close relative dies in a car accident this will have both short and long-term effects on other people's growth and development.

Managing changes

Managing the challenges and changes we face in life can be difficult. It is important to seek the help of others when it is needed. The support people can access can be split into two main types:

- formal support
- informal support.

Most people can access a whole range of professional support to help them deal with difficult life events, such as serious illness or accidents.

Professional carers, such as doctors, nurses and counsellors are all examples of people who can provide formal support. Formal support comes from people who are trained and skilled in their work and they are paid for what they do. The specialist training formal carers have also means they have the knowledge and experience to help others handle the life events they may never have experienced before. Dealing with the death of a loved one can make some people depressed, and counsellors can be a great support in helping people deal with their grief.

Family and friends are also able to offer support to others in difficult times, helping with everyday physical tasks such as shopping, housework and washing and bathing. These people offer informal support. Informal supporters are not trained for what they do and don't get paid for their work. However, the work they do is really important. Many people in later adulthood rely on the informal support they receive from their families and friends to be able to remain independent and continue to live in their own homes.

In the UK there are thousands of people who act as informal supporters every day, working in different ways to improve the lives of others. Many of these informal supporters are under the age of 16. Spending time with family and friends who are housebound or going through a difficult time in life can be a great source of emotional and social help.

Activity   The effect of unexpected life events

Consider how the physical, intellectual, emotional and social development of a person might be affected by each of the following unexpected life events:

- being promoted at work
- imprisonment
- being excluded from school.

▶ How you will be assessed

What you need to know about the examination

There are a number of key things you need to be aware of:

- The examination is 60 minutes long and there is a maximum mark of 50.

- Examiners work on the principle of a mark a minute, so you have some extra time here to think and plan your answers. Remember to read the questions, think about them, plan your answers, write your answers and review what you have written.

- There will be a range of questions on the paper – short multiple-choice-type questions, short answer questions and some longer questions.

- There will be a range of different command words used in the questions – make sure you know what they are asking you to do!

How to approach answering the examination paper

You need to revise everything in this unit, including the areas where you have been set tasks to do some research, as not all the information you need would fit in this book. Your teacher/tutor is likely to give you some practice questions to complete and a mock/practice paper to complete. This is a good way to practise your examination technique and how to use your time well. This will mean that you are well prepared to sit the question paper.

When you open the paper it is a good idea to remember the following:

- Quickly look through the whole paper to see what it looks like. Be careful not to turn over two pages together and miss a whole question, and check the last page so you don't miss any questions. This will calm you down, as you will know what is coming. It will also help you plan how to use the 60 minutes you have to get the best results. Some people rush their answers and sit for 30 minutes doing very little, thinking they have finished, when they could have written better answers. Some people spend too long on the first part of the paper and never reach the end, losing out on many marks. Plan what time you want to start the second half of the paper and space your time evenly.

- There will be one long question at the end of the paper. Even if it looks hard, you will need to attempt it, especially if you are hoping to do well in the exam.

How to approach answering questions

You will be given some background information on which the questions are based. Look at the sample and the practice questions for the unit. After each question are some tips on how to answer them well.

Background information

John is 31 years of age and a care assistant in a day centre for older people. He works closely with Betty and Ray, who are both 83 years of age.

Betty and Ray both have problems with walking and mobility. They find completing everyday tasks quite difficult. They have two children and a number of close friends who live very near their home.

'Identify the current life stages of John and Betty'. (2 marks)

This is a very straightforward question. You will need to have learned off by heart the life stages and the ages attached to them to answer this question.

In answering the question you just need to state the life stage for each person and do not need to write in full sentences.

'Give two examples of physical changes which occur in middle adulthood'. (2 marks)

In order to answer this type of question you will need to have learned the types of physical changes which happen at each life stage. These are identified for you in this unit. It would be a good idea to create a mind map diagram showing the main changes which happen physically, intellectually, emotionally and socially in each life stage.

As this is a question worth only two marks, a list will do and you will not need to write in full sentences.

'Explain how two different types of informal support could help Betty and Ray with their everyday living'. (4 marks)

In this sort of question hints are often given in the background information which help you in your answers. It is important to go back and look at the information given. Make sure that you look at two different types of informal support and try to make sure you do not repeat yourself in your answer.

You will need to write in full sentences and make sure you link the types of support to how they could help Betty and Ray with everyday living.

'Assess the possible impact attending the day centre may have for Betty and Ray's development'. (8 marks)

There will usually be at least one longer question on the paper where you will be required to write at length about a particular topic or issue.

This type of question will be worth the most marks on the paper and you will need to do a lot of thinking before you write. You are likely to be asked to look at something from a number of different points of view and asked to 'assess' or 'evaluate' the effect of something.

In this particular question you are asked to look at how attending the day centre may affect Betty and Ray's development. Most learners will think that attending the day centre will have a positive effect for Betty and Ray, but you will also need to consider that it might have a negative impact on them as well. For example, being at the day centre may make them feel upset that they can no longer do the things they have always done for themselves.

To gain really good marks you will need to be able to consider things from different points of view. You will need to write in full sentences and use paragraphs to structure your written answer.

Introduction

How do you recognise good practice in health and social care? This unit will help you to find out about the values that underpin good health and social care practice. These values include confidentiality, treating individuals with dignity and respect, and safeguarding individuals to ensure their physical and emotional safety while they are in your care.

Good practice in health and social care should always aim to empower individuals, enabling them to be involved in decisions and to do as much for themselves as possible. This can include adapting activities: for example, providing playing cards with larger print for an individual with visual impairment or adapting cutlery so that people with physical needs are able to feed themselves.

The values that underpin good health and social care practice are also important to everyday life. We all prefer to be treated with respect, to feel safe and to have our needs considered, and we should all understand how distressing life can be if any of this does not happen. This unit will help you to recognise where the values we all appreciate can be applied to health and social care.

Assessment: You will be assessed by a series of assignments set by your teacher/tutor.

Learning aims

In this unit you will:

A explore the care values that underpin current practice in health and social care

B investigate ways of empowering individuals who use health and social care services.

> When I went on placement to a day centre for young adults with learning disabilities, I learned that I should not gossip about the users of the service to my friends when I call them on my mobile phone.
>
> Deena Williams, *would-be care assistant, aged 16 years*

Health and Social Care Values

2

BTEC
Assessment Zone

This table shows you what you must do in order to achieve a **Pass**, **Merit** or **Distinction** grade, and where you can find activities in this book to help you.

Assessment criteria			
Level 1	Level 2 Pass	Level 2 Merit	Level 2 Distinction
Learning aim A: Explore the core values that underpin current practice in health and social care			
1A.1 English Identify how care values are used to support users of services.	**2A.P1** English Describe how care values support users of services, using relevant examples. **Assessment activity 2.1** **See page 41.**	**2A.M1** English Discuss the importance of the values that underpin current practice in health and social care, with reference to selected examples. **Assessment activity 2.1** **See page 41.**	**2A.D1** Assess the potential impact on the individual of effective and ineffective application of the care values in health and social care practice, with reference to selected examples. **Assessment activity 2.1** **See page 41.**
1A.2 Demonstrate the use of care values in a selected health and social care context.	**2A.P2** Demonstrate the use of care values in selected health and social care contexts. **Assessment activity 2.1** **See page 41.**		
Learning aim B: Investigate ways of empowering individuals who use health and social care services			
1B.3 Identify ways in which care workers can empower individuals.	**2B.P3** Describe ways in which care workers can empower individuals, using relevant examples from health and social care. **Assessment activity 2.2** **See page 51.**	**2B.M2** Discuss the extent to which individual circumstances can be taken into account when planning care that will empower them, using relevant examples from health and social care. **Assessment activity 2.2** **See page 51.**	**2B.D2** Assess the potential difficulties in taking individual circumstances into account when planning care that will empower an individual, making suggestions for improvement. **Assessment activity 2.2** **See page 51.**
1B.4 Describe how an individual's circumstances can be used to create a care plan that empowers the individual.	**2B.P4** Explain why it is important to take individual circumstances into account when planning care that will empower an individual, using relevant examples from health and social care. **Assessment activity 2.2** **See page 51.**		

English   English signposting

How you will be assessed

The unit will be assessed by a series of internally assessed tasks. You will be expected to show an understanding of values and how these should be applied in the context of the health and social care sector. The tasks will be based on a scenario where you work in a local health or social care organisation.

Your assessment could be in the form of:

- an induction pack for volunteers in health and social care settings
- training materials, such as leaflets, booklets and PowerPoint® presentations
- a training DVD that demonstrates the application of values to the delivery of health and social care
- an article or set of articles for a magazine.

Values in health and social care

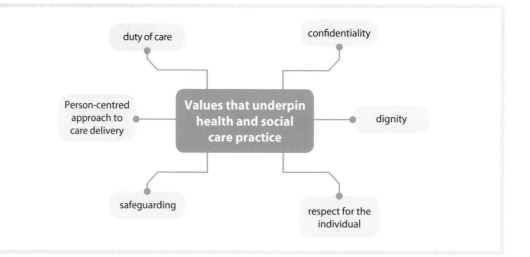

Introduction

In this topic you will learn what is meant by 'health and social care values' and how these are applied to the way in which care is delivered.

Values are the ideas or concepts that ensure health and social care is delivered in the best possible way. They help to ensure that care improves life for individuals, rather than making it worse. This is known as **beneficence**, which means doing good and not harm to someone.

You will often hear the word **underpinning** when values in health and social care are being discussed. We use this word to show how the values support the way care is delivered, in the same way that foundations support the bricks, mortar and wood of a house. Without the values, health and social care would fall down. You can see evidence of this from cases in the media where individuals in residential settings have been mistreated. This mistreatment was, in fact, care delivery that was not underpinned by health and social care values.

Key terms

Values – the ideas that lie behind and inform good health and social care practice.

Beneficence – doing good and not harm to an individual.

Underpin – to provide a supporting framework.

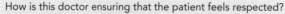

- duty of care
- confidentiality
- Person-centred approach to care delivery
- **Values that underpin health and social care practice**
- dignity
- safeguarding
- respect for the individual

How is this doctor ensuring that the patient feels respected?

Case study

Five years ago, Miss Jane da Silva was diagnosed with a condition that affected her muscles and nerves and she decided she needed to enter residential care. She moved into the Elms Nursing Home, hoping for a more comfortable life with good care.

The Elms Nursing Home is a busy place; the ratio of staff to service users meets the legal requirements, but there are never any extra staff to deal immediately with incidents, such as someone spilling their food or soiling their bed sheets. This means that individuals are sometimes left in uncomfortable situations until a member of staff can help them.

All of the service users are woken up at the same time each morning and placed on the toilet before dressing. None of the service users are ever asked if they need to use the toilet. One morning Miss da Silva decided to object to this routine and was told crossly that she should be glad that someone was looking after her.

Some of the staff were kind, but were just too busy and they would insist on calling Jane by her first name, even though she would have preferred to be called Miss da Silva, but when she mentioned this to the manager, he laughed and said, 'We're all one big family and don't use titles.'

1 How do you think care delivery at the Elms Nursing Home would affect the service users?
2 What changes would you make if you were the manager?
3 How do you think the ratio of staff to service users at the Elms Nursing Home affects the quality of care delivered?
4 Who are the most important people at the Elms Nursing Home?
5 Why is it important that individuals who use services are able to make complaints about the quality of care?

Activity   Values

Look at the photographs. The staff are all busy supporting the users of the service.

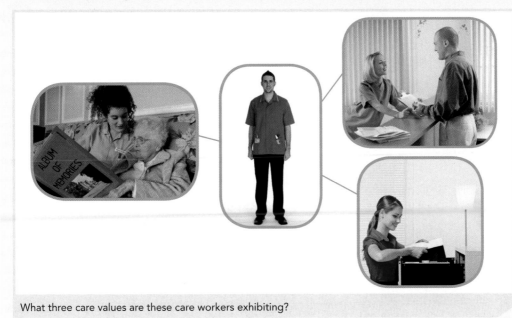

What three care values are these care workers exhibiting?

Exploring care values (1)

Confidentiality

We all assume that we understand what confidentiality is and know how to apply it to everyday situations. However, in health and social care the rules are rather different. For example, you might tell your best friend everything, but you cannot tell them everything about the users of the service where you work. This would be breaking the rules of confidentiality.

In health and social care confidentiality means that we do not share *without permission* information that has been entrusted to us. This includes not sharing personal information about users of the services with friends, family or other individuals outside the setting, or chatting about work in public places.

The rules of confidentiality are:

- not discussing one individual with another
- not sharing written information without permission
- secure storage of records, including those stored electronically.

Breaching confidentiality

There are occasions when **confidential** information must be shared: for example, if an individual was at risk of being harmed or of harming another person.

All health and social care settings have procedures that must be followed with regard to the breaching of confidentiality. There is a clear difference between following a procedure that would mean informing the manager or senior member of staff on duty, and telling a friend. Do you know the difference?

Key terms

Confidential – Information that is secret. It has been entrusted to only the person to whom it has been communicated. It is private and not open for general discussion or publication.

Case study

Sarah Smith has just completed a busy night shift at the Countess of Newbury Nursing Home. The home provides residential and nursing care for 12 females who have dementia.

It has been a difficult shift for Sarah, as several of the residents woke up at least three times in the night and became confused and noisy.

When the shift finishes, Sarah and a colleague go to catch the bus and begin chatting about the events of the night. There are several people at the bus stop, including a relative of one of the residents in the nursing home.

Sarah and the nurse are laughing about an incident that involves this relative and mention the resident's name.

When Sarah returns to work the next night, she finds that the relative has made a complaint about their behaviour at the bus stop. The manager said that Sarah and her colleague's behaviour had broken the rules that accompany one of the health and social care values.

1 Can you name the underpinning value that Sarah should have applied to her behaviour?

2 If the relative had not been at the bus stop, would Sarah's behaviour still have been unacceptable?

Dignity

We all want our dignity to be protected, for example by being allowed to dress in private. Individuals who use health and social care services are often vulnerable in some way. Health and social care workers must protect the dignity of each individual by being aware of situations and actions that could cause embarrassment and make the individual feel silly or exposed.

For example, it is important to ensure that when we are supporting individuals to perform personal care tasks, such as dressing, using the toilet and bathing, we close doors, screens and curtains. We should never stare at an individual or expose parts of their body any more than is really necessary.

It is also important to *offer* support to individuals rather than *insisting* on giving support. Allowing individuals to be as independent as possible protects their dignity because it shows that you are recognising them as a person with abilities. Making fun of someone because they have an accident, or take a long time to complete personal tasks, is not only unkind, it also reduces an individual's sense of dignity by embarrassing them.

Sometimes individuals cannot feed themselves; this may be due to illness, injury or age. Care workers can protect the dignity of individuals by speaking politely to the individual, not rushing them and allowing them to finish the first mouthful before offering another. It is also important to allow individuals to leave the food unfinished if they are no longer hungry. Never try to force someone to complete their meal as this will make them feel undignified. All concerns should be reported to the manager or supervisor.

On work placement or in employment, always remember that everyone needs support at some time in their life; deliver care to service users in the way you would wish to be cared for.

How can this care worker protect the dignity of the service user?

Activity	Helping someone to eat

Resources:

- breakfast cereal
- spoons
- milk
- cereal bowls.

In pairs, take turns to feed each other with the breakfast cereal and then answer the following questions:

1 How did being fed make you feel?

2 Did you feel dignified?

3 If you had to be fed by someone else, what points would you like them to consider?

4 What have you learned from this activity?

Exploring care values (2)

Respect for the individual

We all prefer to be treated with **respect**, for instance being addressed by our name rather than being addressed as 'you' or 'love'. The use of our name shows that we are being fully recognised as an individual, which is important. In order to show respect to the individuals we give care to, it is important for workers in health and social care to remember the following rules:

- Do not **discriminate** against an individual, in other words do not treat one individual differently from another.
- Do not judge individuals for what they may have done.
- Use the **appropriate terms** when addressing an individual, for example Dr, Mrs, Mr, Miss, Begum.
- Do not use words that could cause **offence**.
- Show interest in each individual, which includes learning how to pronounce names that are unfamiliar to you.
- Do not make fun of individuals, for instance if they make a mistake, can't do something, forget something or have an accident.

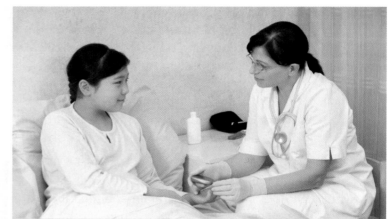

If you don't know how to pronounce a name, ask for help and write it down so you can remember it later.

Activity   Respect and discrimination

Ask your teacher's permission to conduct an internet search:

1 Find out the correct ways of addressing people from three ethnic groups that are different from your own.
2 Find out the correct names of two medical conditions that may cause an individual to be disabled.
3 Investigate two organisations that support individuals who have experienced discrimination.
4 Create a short presentation for your class on your findings.
5 Produce a handout to accompany your presentation to be given to your class colleagues.

Safeguarding

This means that we must ensure the physical and emotional safety of all individuals in our care. For example, signing in and out of a work placement tells the manager who is on the premises and helps to prevent unauthorised people, who could potentially cause harm, coming in. Safeguarding also means that we do not behave in a way that causes the users of the service to feel threatened or afraid. This can include things like not shouting or waving your arms around, as this sort of behaviour can be frightening to a vulnerable person. You must also be careful to take reasonable health and safety precautions, such as replacing disinfectant in the correct cupboard, and reporting trailing flexes and frayed edges of carpets to the manager or senior professional on duty.

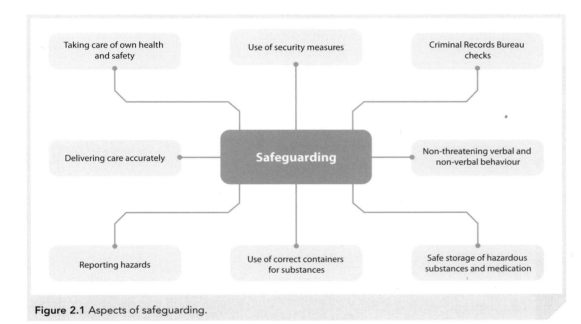

Figure 2.1 Aspects of safeguarding.

Remember

- Everyone who works or is on placement in health and social care has a responsibility to safeguard the users of the service.
- Never assume that safeguarding is only the responsibility of senior staff or, if you are on placement, only of the employed staff.
- The procedures that support safeguarding must be observed at all times.
- Not following safeguarding procedures could mean that you are breaking the law.
- Service users are often vulnerable and are relying on carers to ensure their physical and emotional safety.
- Taking care of your own health and safety helps to safeguard others.
- Everyone needs care at some time in their life; be as careful of the safety of others as you would like others to be of yours.

Exploring care values (3)

Person-centred care

Person-centred care is a way of delivering health and social care that places the individual at the centre of the activity. Rather than professionals deciding what is best for an individual, producing a plan and delivering the care, the individual is involved in every stage of the process. The individual's needs and preferences, likes and dislikes are considered. For example, they may prefer the physiotherapist to attend on a day other than Friday so that they can attend the mosque for prayers. Another example may be that an individual may need crèche facilities in order to attend counselling for depression. This approach to care considers the whole person, rather than just one or two needs. This is why it is called 'person-centred'.

Case study

Mrs Karen Smith is a 42-year-old woman with longstanding mental health problems who has recently suffered a stroke, which has reduced the movement in her left arm and affected her speech.

Following her stroke, Mrs Smith was assessed by the mental health team, the physiotherapist and the speech and language therapist.

The professionals then met to discuss what would be the best way to support Mrs Smith and enable her to live as normal a life as possible.

Mrs Smith was invited to a discussion with the professionals and asked what her needs and wishes were. Mrs Smith wanted to remain at home and continue with her life. She attended a mental health drop-in centre where she had been involved in various activities.

The professionals involved Mrs Smith in the planning of her care and took into account her wishes, likes, dislikes and preferences as much as possible. It was agreed that:

- the physiotherapy appointments could be on Monday mornings, which would enable Mrs Smith to attend the drop-in centre on Monday afternoons; transport was arranged as Mrs Smith has found bus travel difficult since her stroke
- the speech and language therapist would call on Wednesday mornings to enable Mrs Smith to attend the drop-in centre on Wednesday afternoons; again, transport would be arranged
- a community care assistant would call twice daily to assist Mrs Smith with personal care
- the mobile meals service would provide a main meal.

1 How would the care arrangements support Mrs Smith to carry on with her life?

2 Why was it important for Mrs Smith to be involved in planning her own care?

3 How would Mrs Smith have been affected, if she had not been involved in planning her own care?

WorkSpace

▶ PHIL PETERS

Healthcare Assistant

I am a healthcare assistant working for a busy NHS Trust. I usually work on one of the general surgical wards, but I may be asked to help out in other areas of the hospital. I really enjoy my work, making patients feel more comfortable and working with the nurses to deliver high-quality care and support. I worked on the hospital main reception at first, but prefer working on the ward as I can follow my patients' progress.

I work 37.5 hours a week on a rota basis, including working some evenings, nights and weekends. You have to be flexible, but that's OK – I prefer shift work to nine to five because it means that I see my patients at different stages of their recovery.

These are some of the tasks I have to do:

- Washing, dressing and feeding patients who cannot do this for themselves and providing support for those who need extra help.
- Helping people to regain their mobility after surgery.
- Bed making.
- Generally assisting with the overall comfort of patients; for example, by smoothing pillows, adjusting bed tables, placing articles such as spectacles and newspapers within easy reach.
- Monitoring the condition of patients by taking temperature, pulse and respiration and accurately recording these details on the patients' medical charts.
- Helping patients to use the toilet or providing bedpans for those who cannot get out of bed.

I found that my BTEC Level 2 qualification in Health and Social Care was really useful in my job, particularly the unit about values. I was able to see how the staff on the ward applied these values in their patient care. I didn't need any particular qualifications to get the job, but having the BTEC Level 2 Certificate really helped.

Think about it

1 Why are the health and social care values important to Phil's role as a healthcare assistant?

2 Which values do you think would apply when helping patients to perform personal care tasks, such as washing or dressing?

Exploring care values (4)

Duty of care

There is a **legal requirement** for all health and social care workers to provide a **duty of care**. This means that while a member of staff is on the premises, even if they are on their break, they have a responsibility to ensure the safety of the individuals who use the service. This can include things like waiting to go for lunch until there are enough staff available to ensure the safety of the individuals using the service. It also means completing tasks to the highest possible standard so that individuals receive the care they need. A duty of care applies to all areas of professional practice, underpinning the delivery of health and social care. Without this, just like the house without foundations, health and social care falls down and individuals are placed at risk.

Key terms

Legal requirement – something that has to be done by law.

Duty of care – responsibility to keep people in our care safe from harm.

Code of practice – list of rules which state how health and social care must be delivered.

Activity   Codes of practice and legislation

A **code of practice** is a list of rules that should be followed by all staff when providing health or social care for individuals.

Ask your teacher's permission to use the internet to find the codes of practice that relate to the following professions:

- Nursing and midwifery
- Social care
- Social work
- Speech and language therapy
- Physiotherapy.

Produce a poster of your findings to display in the classroom.

Why is it important to protect the patient's dignity at all times?

Completion of all tasks to the highest standard

Application to all areas of professional practice

Duty of care

All staff/learners on premises have a responsibility for the safety of service users

Adhering to codes of practice, and legislation

Figure 2.2 What does duty of care mean?

Assessment activity 2.1   *English*   2A.P1 | 2A.P2 | 2A.M1 | 2A.D1

Miss Jennifer van der Pays is 23 and has Down's syndrome. She works at a local supermarket and lives with her parents in the suburb of Welmsley. Jennifer recently had a fall and had to attend the accident and emergency department of her local hospital. The receptionist in the department addressed Jennifer as 'Miss van der Pays' and used a polite tone when speaking to her. The nurse asked Jennifer to come into a cubicle and remove her shoes and tights so that the doctor could examine the injury. The nurse asked if she needed any help to get onto the couch and closed the cubicle curtains.

1 Name two values which underpinned the care received by Jennifer.

2 Name any part of the event where the values you have named could have been used to support Jennifer more.

3 For the values you have named, discuss their importance in providing high-quality care for Jennifer.

4 For the values you have named, assess the impact on Jennifer's care, and say if they were applied effectively or ineffectively.

Tips

You must discuss each value in turn, relating it to the delivery of health and social care and referring to your chosen examples. You should demonstrate in your discussion how each value interrelates to support the delivery of health and social care.

You should extend your work to assess the potential impact on individuals when the values are applied to care delivery. You should give careful consideration of the differences in impact when the values are applied effectively or ineffectively. You should refer to examples; check with your teacher before using examples from the internet.

Take it further

Read the scenario about Jennifer again and answer the following questions:

1 Which code of practice would the nurse be following when she was supporting Jennifer?

2 How can this code of practice ensure that Jennifer receives a high standard of care?

3 What factors could prevent Jennifer receiving a high standard of care?

Empowering individuals

Getting started

Do you like to make your own decisions? How do you feel when others make decisions for you?

How do you think service users feel when health or social care workers make decisions *for* them rather than *with* them?

Key terms

Empower – to give service users control of their own lives.

Introduction

When we apply values to health and social care practice, we **empower** individuals who use the services. Health and social care professionals do this by delivering care in a way that enables individuals to take control of their own lives as much as possible. These are some of the ways in which this can happen.

Adapting activities and environments

Activities can include leisure pursuits, such as a game of skittles or a quiz, or everyday tasks, such as feeding or dressing. Adaptations, such as bright-coloured bowling balls, which can be seen more easily by an individual with a visual impairment, or a quiz set at a level that enables individuals with learning disabilities to join in the fun, can mean full participation and an enhanced quality of life.

In the same way, providing an individual who has arthritis with a shoe horn attached to a long handle can enable them to put on their own shoes rather than waiting for assistance.

Environments can also be adapted. For example, improving the lighting in the day centre to enable individuals with a hearing impairment to lip-read will support them in joining in with a conversation rather than feeling like an outsider.

Braille playing cards could enable people with visual impairments to join in.

Taking account of the individual

Recognising an individual's rights is a legal requirement in the United Kingdom and in many other countries. Individuals have a right to health and social care support if they need it. They also have a right to support that is underpinned by values such as respect, dignity and confidentiality. Health and social care professionals agree with these values and work hard to deliver appropriate care and support, meeting the needs of individuals.

In a busy setting, it can be much harder to take account of preferences, likes and dislikes. For example, an individual may prefer to have breakfast after hanging the washing out on the line, but the care worker may find it more convenient to serve breakfast first. It is important to remember that the care worker is there to support the individual and not the other way around. In the same way, it is important to recognise that attending to likes and dislikes is a way of empowering individuals by recognising their individuality. For example, requiring halal meat does not mean that the individual only likes eating food prepared to one recipe; requiring a vegetarian diet does not mean including lentils in every meal. Allowing individuals to state their likes, dislikes and preferences enables them to have some control over their everyday lives. We all like to have this, but it is particularly important for vulnerable individuals who are unable to perform for themselves tasks that others take for granted, such as those involved with personal care.

This is particularly important when supporting individuals who cannot speak for themselves. For example, someone who has a speech and language impairment or who has dementia will receive better care if the care workers have an understanding of the person's likes and dislikes. When caring for a person who cannot express themselves, it is important to involve family and friends who can provide the important details that can make such a difference to care delivery. Just imagine how you would feel if you were constantly having to listen to music you did not like or presented with food that you would not choose to eat and couldn't express your feelings or preferences.

Activity   Considering an individual's preferences

In small groups, discuss how important it is to each of you to have your likes and dislikes considered:

- at meal times
- in deciding which film to see
- when being bought new clothes by relatives
- in choosing what music is played.

Discuss why these things are important to you.

Working in partnership with other people

Introduction

Working in health and social care involves working with others, which may include relatives and friends of an individual, in addition to health and social care professionals. It is important to be willing to work with different people, showing respect for their opinions and accepting their help when you need it. In this way, mistakes can be avoided and you will progress in your career.

Health and social care professionals work cooperatively with fellow professionals, relatives and the individual users of the service to provide a standard of care that meets the needs of the individuals in the setting.

When you show a willingness to work with others, you are contributing to a pleasant working environment. And remember, health and social care teams are more efficient when individuals work together, sharing tasks and supporting each other.

Just checking

1 Describe three ways of adapting activities to meet particular needs.
2 Why does providing care that takes account of an individual's likes, dislikes and preferences empower them?
3 Why is it important to be willing to work with other people in health and social care?

Case study 1

Ramón Suarez is admitted to Ward 17 complaining of severe abdominal pain. He is examined by the surgeon, who decides that Ramón's appendix has perforated and he must have his appendix removed.

Ramón becomes very distressed because having the operation means that he will have to stay in hospital. Ramón has been living with his disabled 82-year-old mother since the death of his father a year ago. The old lady would now be alone at home and unable to care for herself.

The surgeon refers the matter to the ward manager, who contacts social services. A social worker calls to see Ramón's mother and arranges for her to be taken into a local care home until Ramón has fully recovered. He also arranges for someone from the care home to bring Ramón's mother to visit him while he is in hospital.

1 Why do you think the surgeon refers the matter to the ward manager?
2 What partnerships can you find in this case study?

Why is it important to work together to solve problems?

Case study 2

Rebecca and Nigel James live with their three-year-old daughter, Helen, in a pleasant suburb at the edge of a large city.

Helen has autism and attends a special nursery in the city four times a week. As Helen's speech is not progressing at the rate expected for her age, the GP has referred her to Teresa, a speech and language therapist. Teresa has worked with Rebecca and Nigel, showing them how to encourage Rebecca. She has asked them for information about Helen, calling them 'the experts'.

Rebecca and Nigel feel that Teresa shared the support and planning for Helen with them and this has encouraged them to work with her as partners.

1 Why was it important that Teresa worked with Rebecca and Nigel?

2 Why did Teresa call Rebecca and Nigel the experts?

Case study 3

Simon King has just been released from prison where he has served a three-year sentence for burglary. Simon has been referred to the Probation Service and has to meet with his probation officer three times a week.

Simon's wife divorced him while he was in prison, so he needs a new home and the prison service has referred Simon to the local housing officer.

1 Why is it important for the professionals to work in partnership when supporting Simon?

2 What could happen to Simon if the professionals do not communicate with each other?

Discussion point

In small groups, discuss:

* why it is important for each of the groups to work in partnership
* why it is important to include the individuals receiving care in the partnerships.

Promoting choice

Introduction

Do you like to have choices? Do you like to decide what, when and where to eat, what to wear, whether to stay in or go out? Of course you do, and most of the time you can make those choices for yourself without even thinking about it.

Did you know? ❓

There is a clear link between giving an individual the right to make informed choices and their overall wellbeing.

In groups, discuss why you think this could be.

Link ⊙

This topic links to Unit 5: Promoting Health and Wellbeing and Unit 8: Individual Rights in Health and Social Care.

Individuals who use health and social care services also like to make choices; they have a right to make choices, but are not always allowed to exercise that right. Health and social care professionals speak about 'informed choices', this means that individuals should be given all of the information they need in order to decide about, for example, accepting treatment or entering residential care.

Here are some of the reasons why this may not happen:

- The member of staff does not realise that there are choices available.
- The individual may have difficulty in expressing choices.
- The member of staff may be in a hurry and decides that it would be quicker to decide for the individual.

None of these is an acceptable reason not to offer the available choices. Individuals have a right to choose what they will eat, what they will wear and whether or not they will take part in an activity. They also have a right to choose whether or not to accept treatment. It is part of the professional's role in health and social care to promote choice and enable individuals to exercise their rights.

Think about the choices you make every day:

- what to wear
- what to eat
- what music to listen to
- which friends you will meet after school or college
- who you will call or text on your mobile phone.

How different would your life be if those choices were removed? Try to imagine what life would be like without those choices. Would you like this restricted life? Would anyone?

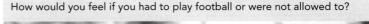

How would you feel if you had to play football or were not allowed to?

Why do we support individuals?

Do you ever need support? Of course you do, everyone needs support sometimes. How individuals are supported makes a huge difference to their self-esteem, confidence and self-image. The right type of support is empowering; in other words, it enables people to stay or become independent, allowing them to do as much for themselves as possible. Ways of providing empowering support could include:

- adapting environments – for example, widening access so that individuals who use wheelchairs can go in and out of rooms and buildings without additional help
- offering people a choice of activities that reflect their individual interests and personalities
- providing **advocates** for individuals who cannot speak for themselves, perhaps due to speech and language difficulties or mental health issues
- providing opportunities for individuals to give feedback on the level of service they have received
- providing interpreters and translators for individuals for whom English is an additional language
- promoting **autonomy**; this means encouraging individuals to make their own decisions.

Some people may choose to live at home rather than a care home. What support do you think they may require?

Activity   Adapting activities

Produce a fun activity adapted for one of the following groups:

- visually impaired
- hearing impaired
- users of wheelchairs.

Use the activity yourself and give yourself a score from 1 to 5 on how user-friendly it is. (1 is excellent and 5 means that improvements are needed.)

Write a short report on how this activity could be adapted for use by individuals from one of the other groups in the list.

Key terms

Advocate – a person responsible for acting and speaking on behalf of someone who is unable to do so.

Autonomy – freedom to make your own decisions.

Communication

Preferred ways of communicating

Effective communication is an important skill in health and social care. Using the appropriate form of communication is particularly important. In supporting service users it is best to use the form of communication that the individual prefers. This shows that we are interested in the individual and recognise them as a person.

Sometimes an individual's preferred way of communicating may be related to disability; for instance, a hearing impaired person might want you to facilitate their lip-reading. Whatever the reason, using an individual's preferred way of communication shows respect, protects dignity and demonstrates that we are delivering care and support that is underpinned by health and social care values.

Communication should be clear, understandable and fitted to the situation; using an individual's preferred way of communicating supports the development of trust between staff and service users, and should be regarded as part of the duty of care.

How is this care assistant adapting their behaviour to put the service user at ease?

Activity Speaking the same language

- Find out how many different language groups there are in your home area.
- Find out how to say 'hello' in at least four of the different languages.
- Find out how to write 'hello' in as many of the languages as you can.
- Produce a poster for the classroom illustrating your findings.

Alternative methods of communication

Alternative methods of communication that individuals may wish to use could include British Sign Language, preferred by some individuals with a hearing impairment or who are without hearing, and Makaton, used by those with learning difficulties. Remember, individuals who use English as their additional language may be more comfortable using their first language. It is important that users of services are able to communicate in their preferred way; this will mean that they can express their needs and wants in a way that enables them to take part in decisions about their care and support.

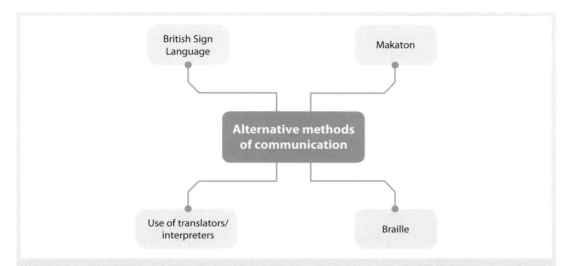

Figure 2.3 Alternative methods of communication.

Activity	Speech is not the only method

1 In groups, use the internet to find out how many different methods of communication exist that do not use speech.

2 Produce a poster for your classroom that shows the different methods of communication.

3 In groups, use the internet to find out about one organisation that supports individuals who use an alternative form of communication.

4 Discuss with your tutor/teacher the possibility of a fundraising event to support your chosen organisation.

Positive working practices

How do you like to be supported in class? Choose the item from the list below that is the closest to your choice of support:

- Have the work taken away and finished for you.

- Have someone explain the task in a way that you understand and then allow you to complete it.

- Be offered more support than you really need, which makes you feel useless.

Key terms

Enablement – ways and means to act independently.

There are ways of working with individuals that promote empowerment and **enablement** and recognise each one as a person in their own right. Here are some examples:

- Needs-led assessment, which bases care planning on what an individual actually needs rather than following a general formula.

- Valuing diversity by appreciating the differences between individuals and planning care to fit these differences.

- Recognising that individuals have a right to care that meets their needs and is underpinned by health and social care values.

- Care planning that includes assessment of acceptable risks, rather than restricting individuals.

- Listening to individuals and discussing each stage of the care plan with them.

Just checking

1 What are the values that underpin current health and social care practice?
2 Name three ways of preserving an individual's dignity when delivering health or social care.
3 Explain what is meant by non-discriminatory practice and give an example.
4 Explain what is meant by a person-centred approach to care delivery.
5 Describe three examples of adapting activities.
6 Explain why a hearing-impaired individual would benefit from improved lighting in their setting.
7 Describe how using their preferred method of communication empowers an individual.
8 Give one example of how the provision of an advocate can support an individual.
9 Describe three positive working practices.

Why is it important to discuss a care plan with a patient or service user?

Assessment activity 2.2

2B.P3 | 2B.P4 | 2B.M2 | 2B.D2

The Greenings Day Centre provides life skills training for young adults who have learning disabilities. The centre aims to prepare young adults for independent living by offering the following opportunities:

- money management
- travelling on public transport
- care of clothes
- shopping for clothes
- shopping for food
- working with others.

You are on work experience at the day centre, and are involved in supporting two of the young adults who are learning how to travel on public transport.

1 Name three ways in which you could empower these two young adults when working with them.

2 Explain why it would be important to consider the personal circumstances of both young adults when producing a plan that would empower them to use public transport.

3 Discuss how much you could consider the personal circumstances of these young adults when producing a transport plan. Are their personal circumstances the only factors to be considered, or are there others?

4 What are the potential difficulties in taking the young adults' personal circumstances into account?

5 Suggest ways of overcoming or managing three potential difficulties.

Tips

Question 3 asks you to discuss how much you can take individual circumstances into account when planning empowering care, or whether there are other factors to be considered. You should refer to such issues as:

- levels of resources, including staff
- the needs of other users of the service
- level of risk to the individual (acceptable/unacceptable).

You will need to refer to relevant examples, which could be those referred to in your work for this unit.

You must assess, or give careful consideration to, any potential difficulties that could arise when planning empowering care. For each potential difficulty that you suggest, you must make a suggestion to resolve the difficulty or improve the situation.

Introduction

How can you make sure you communicate with others of all ages and abilities effectively? Health and social care professionals need good communication skills to develop positive relationships and share information with people using services. Clear communication is important to enable service users to understand and agree to the care they are receiving. They also need to be able to communicate well with people's families and/or carers and their own colleagues and other professionals. Good communication between care professionals allows them to perform their roles effectively, work cooperatively with colleagues and build supportive relationships with service users. It is important, therefore, if you are considering a career in health and social care, to gain the knowledge, understanding and practical skills needed to develop effective interpersonal skills.

There are several different forms of communication used in a health and social care environment. This unit looks at verbal and non-verbal communication methods, and you will learn how they are used effectively in health and social care. You will also learn to recognise a range of factors which may create barriers to communication, preventing people accessing health and social care effectively. You will then consider ways in which these barriers may be overcome, including the use of alternative forms of communication.

Assessment: You will be assessed by a series of assignments set by your teacher/tutor.

Learning aims

In this unit you will:

A investigate different forms of communication

B investigate barriers to communication in health and social care

C communicate effectively in health and social care.

> The way you talk to people is really important. When I went on placement to a residential care home for older people I was told to crouch down to the level at which they were sitting so I wouldn't tower over them and intimidate them. I was also told to speak clearly but not patronisingly.
>
> Kirsten, *would-be care assistant, aged 16 years*

Effective Communication in Health and Social Care

3

This table shows what you must do in order to achieve a **Pass**, **Merit** or **Distinction** grade, and where you can find activities in this book to help you.

Assessment criteria			
Level 1	Level 2 Pass	Level 2 Merit	Level 2 Distinction
Learning aim A: Investigate different forms of communication			
1A.1 Identify different forms of verbal and non-verbal communication.	**2A.P1** Describe different forms of verbal and non-verbal communication. **Assessment activity 3.1** **See page 62.**	**2A.M1** Explain the advantages and disadvantages of different forms of communication used, with reference to a one-to-one and a group interaction. **Assessment activity 3.1** **See page 62.**	**2A.D1** Assess the effectiveness of different forms of communication for service users with different needs. **Assessment activity 3.1** **See page 62.**
1A.2 Identify different forms of alternative communication for different needs, using examples from health and social care.	**2A.P2** Describe different forms of alternative communication for different needs, using examples from health and social care. **Assessment activity 3.1** **See page 62.**		
Learning aim B: Investigate barriers to communication in health and social care			
1B.3 Outline the barriers to communication in health and social care.	**2B.P3** Describe the barriers to communication in health and social care and their effects on service users. **Assessment activity 3.2** **See page 69.**	**2B.M2** Explain how measures have been implemented to overcome barriers to communication, with reference to a selected case. **Assessment activity 3.2** **See page 69.**	**2B.D2** Evaluate the effectiveness of measures taken to remove barriers to communication, with reference to a selected case. **Assessment activity 3.2** **See page 69.**
1B.4 Identify ways in which barriers to communication may be overcome for individuals with sensory loss.	**2B.P4** Using examples, explain ways in which barriers to communication may be overcome and the benefits to service users of overcoming these barriers. **Assessment activity 3.2** **See page 69.**		
Learning aim C: Communicate effectively in health and social care			
1C.5 English Demonstrate communication skills through one interaction in health and social care, identifying the forms of communication used.	**2C.P5** English Demonstrate communication skills through interactions in health and social care, describing their effects. **Assessment activity 3.3** **See page 75.**	**2C.M3** English Select and demonstrate communication skills through interactions in health and social care, explaining their effectiveness. **Assessment activity 3.3** **See page 75.**	**2C.D3** English Select and demonstrate communication skills through one-to-one and group interactions in health and social care, evaluating their effectiveness and making recommendations for improvement. **Assessment activity 3.3** **See page 75.**

English   English signposting

How you will be assessed

The unit will be assessed by a series of internally assessed tasks. You will be expected to show an understanding of communication skills in the context of health and social care sectors. The tasks will be based on a scenario where you work in a local health or social care organisation.

Your assessment could be in the form of:

- producing training materials based on a case study and/or DVD based in a health and social care setting, such as a nursery, which:

  - identify, describe and evaluate the effectiveness of different forms of communication used

  - identify and describe a range of barriers to communication, explaining and evaluating ways to overcome them

- a training DVD demonstrating good practice in one-to-one and group interaction.

LINK

This whole unit links to Units 2, 4, 5, 7 and 8 as communication is an essential part of working with other service users and providers.

Why do we communicate? (1)

Introduction

In this topic you will learn about why we communicate, why good communication skills are so important within a health and social care environment and the different contexts for communication. We communicate with others all the time, wherever we may be, often without even realising it and sometimes not intending to.

Communication skills

Interpersonal skills are those that enable us to interact with others, so allowing us to communicate successfully. Good communication skills are vital for those working in health and social care as they help them to:

- develop positive relationships with people using services and their families and friends, so that they can understand and meet their needs
- develop positive relationships with work colleagues and other professionals
- share information with people using the services
- report on the work they do with people.

Why is communication so important between colleagues?

Activity   Portrayal of hospitals on TV

Sit in a circle. Discuss the statement 'TV programmes, such as *Casualty* or *Holby City* create the wrong impression of working life in a large hospital'. One person starts the discussion holding a ball or bean bag. When they have made their point, they throw the ball to someone else in the group and that person responds to what they have said. The ball has to go to each person in the group before anyone who has already spoken can speak again. When the discussion has finished, discuss the following points in your group:

1 Did everyone join in properly? If not, why not?
2 How did sitting in a circle help?
3 How could you tell that someone was about to finish talking?
4 Did you find the task easier or harder with the ball? Why?
5 Look at Figure 3.1. Who in the group used these skills best? How could you tell?

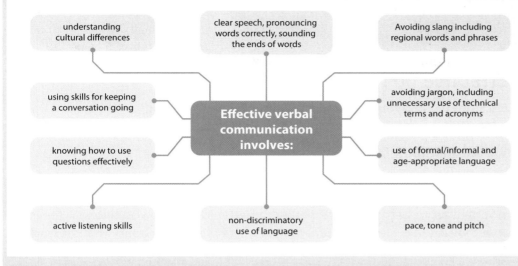

Figure 3.1 The communication skills needed by people working in health and social care environments.

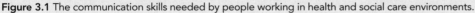

Contexts

One-to-one communication

One-to-one means one person communicating with another person with no other people joining in. The conversation needs a start, for instance a greeting, such as 'Hi', a middle section when you both discuss what you need to talk about, and an ending, such as 'See you later'.

Group communication

Group communication is harder because it only works properly if everyone is able to be involved. Groups work best if there is a team leader who encourages everyone to have a say in turn, rather than several people trying to speak at once and others not joining in.

Formal and informal communication

Formal communication tends to start with a greeting, such as 'Good afternoon. How are you feeling today?' It can be used to show respect for others. Formal conversation is often used when a professional person, such as a health or social care worker, speaks to someone using a service. It is clear, correct and avoids misunderstanding.

Informal communication is more likely to start with 'Hi. How are you?' and allows for a more casual approach and more varied expression, for instance appropriate to the area someone lives. Informal communication is warm and friendly. People usually communicate more informally with friends, including those they work closely with on a day-to-day basis.

Effective verbal communication

Verbal communication uses words to present ideas, thoughts and feelings. Good verbal communication is the ability to both present and explain your ideas clearly through the spoken word, and to listen carefully to other people. This involves using a variety of approaches and styles appropriate to the audience or person you are addressing.

> **Key terms**
>
> **Formal** – polite, respectful or conventional.
>
> **Informal** – casual.

Why do we communicate? (2)

Getting started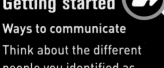

Ways to communicate

Think about the different people you identified as communicating with in the last activity. Sketch a quick spider diagram showing all the different ways you communicate with others in a typical day.

Link

This topic links to Unit 7: Equality and Diversity in Health and Social Care.

Effective non-verbal communication

This topic looks at different forms of non-verbal communication.

Non-verbal communication

This refers to the messages we send out to express ideas and opinions without talking, the main elements of which are shown in Figure 3.2. Understanding body language is very important as it often gives care workers a better idea of how someone is feeling than what they say. It is also important that as a carer you understand what messages your own body language is giving to the person you are trying to help.

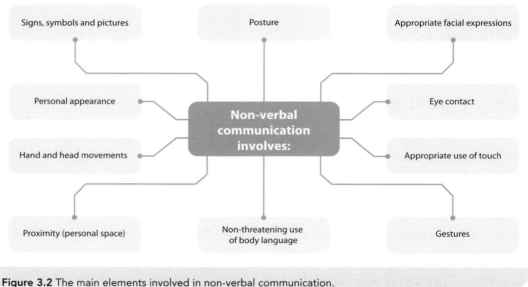

Figure 3.2 The main elements involved in non-verbal communication.

Activity   Showing emotions

1 Draw a set of cartoon faces showing the following emotions: (i) worried (ii) bored (iii) surprised (iv) sad (v) aggressive.

2 Cut pictures out of magazines with people showing different emotions. Put them into groups according to the emotion and then test your work with a partner to see if they can work out which emotion is being portrayed by each.

Body language includes:

• **Posture**: the way you sit or stand or even move can send messages. For example, shaking your head while someone else is talking might indicate that you disagree with them, or waving your arms around can show you are excited. Sitting facing the person you are talking to, with your arms unfolded and a smile on your face, shows a positive and warm response.

- **Facial expression**: the human face is very expressive, able to convey countless emotions without saying a word. The facial expressions for happiness, sadness, anger, surprise, fear and disgust are the same across cultures. It is important to match your facial expressions to the conversation, for example, not smiling when someone is talking about something sad.

- **Eye contact**: most people find that the visual sense affects them most, so eye contact is especially important. We can often tell what someone is feeling by their eyes. Our eyes become wider when we have positive feelings, for example when we are excited or happy, attracted to, or interested in someone. Eye contact is also important in keeping a conversation going and for judging the other person's response.

- **Appropriate use of touch and personal space**: touching another person or moving into their **personal space** can send messages of care and affection, but it can also indicate threat or power over that person. It is important to think about the health and social care environment you are in and what you are trying to convey before touching a person or getting too close to them.

- **Gestures**: there are certain common signs or gestures that most people automatically recognise, but it is important to understand cultural norms so as not to unintentionally cause offence. For example, thumbs-up can mean that all is well and is perfectly acceptable in Western culture, but in the Middle East it is not only unacceptable but also one of the biggest insults possible. It also causes offence in countries such as Greece and Russia.

- **Non-threatening use of body language**: it is important not to give out negative messages through your body language. Turning away slightly with your arms folded portrays negative feelings of boredom, coldness and lack of interest.

- **Personal space**: getting too close to, or far away from, someone can create unease. Getting too close for instance, and so invading their personal space, can cause discomfort, intimidation or distress. The size of a person's personal space often depends on their culture. Americans tend to require more personal space than people from many other cultures. Also, getting too close to someone with a mental illness can be very distressing for them. If a person backs away a little when you are speaking to them don't try to close the gap, as this will make them feel uncomfortable. How close you can move into a person's personal space is very much an individual preference.

Key terms

Personal space – the area immediately surrounding a person that they consider to be their own personal territory. People generally feel uncomfortable if others 'invade' this personal space. Everyone's idea of personal space is different.

| Intimate zone (touching) | Personal zone (less than 1 metre) | Social zone (1-2 metres) | Public zone (2 metres +) |

Does this work for you?

Alternative forms of communication

Introduction

Sometimes it is necessary to find an alternative form of communication to meet people's particular needs, such as communication challenges caused by visual and hearing impairments and learning difficulties. This topic covers some of the wide range of options available.

The Braille system.

Visual impairment

- **Braille**: the Braille system is widely used by blind people to read and write. It was devised in 1821 by Frenchman, Louis Braille. Each Braille character is made up of six dot positions, arranged in a rectangle. A dot may be raised in any of the six positions to form sixty-four possible combinations and these raised dots are read by touch.

- **Braille software**: this creates Braille and comes in a wide range of packages, including those to create mathematical and musical notation as well as text and to translate different languages.

Hearing impairment

- **British Sign Language**: this system uses visual signs made up of shapes, positions and movements of the hands, arms or body and facial expressions. Sign language is commonly used by the families and friends of deaf people as well as by those who are deaf or hard of hearing themselves.

- **Finger spelling**: this is the representation of letters and sometimes numbers by tracing the shapes of letters in the air or on a hand. American, French and Irish Sign Language are all examples of one-handed finger spelling as compared with British Sign Language, which is two-handed.

- **Text messaging**: the vibration function on mobile phones alerts the hearing-impaired when messages and emails arrive.

Learning or speech difficulties

- **Communication passports**: these were invented in 1991 and are a way of documenting and presenting information about children and adults with disabilities who are unable to speak for themselves. They make sense of formal assessment and record the important things about the individual, in an easy to read, portable and person-centred way. Communication passports are now widely used in home, care, social work and health and education settings and are a way of making and of supporting an individual's transitions between services.

- **Bliss symbols**: these are used to provide a written language for people with severe speech disabilities. The system is based on concepts rather than words. It was developed by the Austrian Charles Bliss who wanted to create a universal written language that people speaking any language could learn and communicate in.

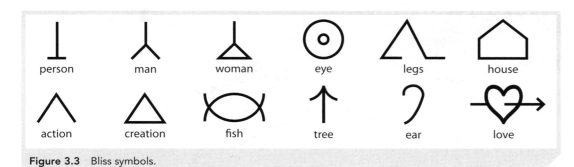

Figure 3.3 Bliss symbols.

- **Makaton**: this is a method of communication using signs and symbols. Unlike British Sign Language, it uses speech as well as actions and symbols, using picture cards. Makaton ties in facial expressions with a word to make the word more easily recognised by those with learning difficulties.

- **Technological aids**: technology provides many electronic aids to help us communicate. For example, computers record, store and communicate information very quickly and efficiently over long distances. Electronic aids can turn small movements into written words and then into speech, such as the voice box most famously used by the scientist, Professor Stephen Hawking.

- **Use of pictures to aid communication**: pictures can be used to communicate with people who have no ability to speak or use a language. For example, many people with autism use picture cards as they tend to learn visually and can communicate better with images and pictures. These have the advantage of being a universal means of communication understandable by people of all ages, abilities and languages.

People who can aid communication

Sometimes it is helpful to involve a specialist to aid communication in health and social care. If someone using a service needs help to communicate because, for example, they use sign language or because they speak a different language, they could use an interpreter. For help with written documents they could use a translator. Some people with speech or learning difficulties could benefit from having an advocate present to help them to communicate.

Activity — Signs, interpreters, translators and advocates

1 Do some research to find out the symbol for at least ten common signs, such as wet floor, used in any health and social care setting, which most people will recognise. Produce an information leaflet for people with learning difficulties to teach them these signs.

2 Find out what the following people do and research how health and social care settings use them:

   (i)   an interpreter for speech

   (ii)   a translator for written word/documents

   (iii)   an advocate.

? Did you know?

We all regularly use non-verbal communication without realising it, for example using symbols in universal chemical formulae. Almost all of us know that water is H_2O. Similarly we recognise road signs and hazard signs, which are often entirely visual.

Investigate different forms of communication

Here are some questions to test what you have learned so far. You will also find a practice assessment assignment to try.

Assessment activity 3.1

You are a trainee early years worker at a nursery in a big town. The children have a wide range of abilities, and a few have learning difficulties. The nursery manager is trying to get some funding from the local council and needs to provide evidence of work she and her staff have done with different children. You have been asked to produce an information pack about the different communication methods that can be used in the nursery by staff and volunteers.

Your pack should include a report on the advantages, disadvantages and effectiveness of each method of communication.

Tip
You could start the activity by producing a mind map of the basic facts about different communication methods. The pack should contain material in a number of formats such as leaflets, booklets and posters.

Just checking

1 What are three features of one-to-one communication?

2 What are three things that help group communication?

3 What is the difference between informal and formal communication? Which would you use with (i) a friend, (ii) someone you have not met before but are trying to help in your job as a doctor's receptionist (iii) your manager?

4 Explain what is meant by verbal communication.

5 Give three examples of non-verbal communication.

6 Describe three examples of when signs, symbols and pictures are useful forms of communication.

7 Describe two alternative methods of communication for someone who (i) is visually impaired, (ii) is hearing impaired, and (iii) has learning difficulties.

WorkSpace

▶ **Emily Burgess**

Early years worker

I am an early years worker in a busy small town nursery. I work in a team that includes six other early years workers, a manager and a cleaner. We have three separate rooms so children of different age groups can have their own room, although they do mix together for certain activities. There is also a room where staff can keep their personal belongings.

My main task is to help to look after the eight children aged between one and three. I love this age group, as they change so quickly. I organise activities for them, such as big-book reading, playing in the dressing-up corner and creative activities, such as finger painting and making cards for special occasions like Mother's Day. We sing songs every day and play simple musical instruments once a week. I also have to make sure the children are fed and changed. Another task is to keep records of what we do each day, the progress made by individual children and details of any concerns I may have about any of them, which I then discuss with the manager.

Each day the children play in the small enclosed area outside for a short time if the weather is good enough. Although the emphasis is on fun, all the activities are designed to deliver the early learning goals, so helping the children develop their skills and knowledge.

I speak to the parents on a daily basis when they drop off and collect their children. I enjoy the fact that I am helping both the children and their parents. I love my job because I enjoy meeting lots of different people and feeling that I am making a difference to them.

Think about it

1 Why are communication skills so important to Emily's job?

2 What are your strengths when it comes to communication? What are the areas that you would like to improve?

3 How can you make sure you communicate with others of all ages and abilities effectively?

Barriers to communication

Introduction

In this topic you will learn about factors that affect communication, called barriers to communication, and their effects, starting with environmental, physical and language barriers.

Factors that affect communication

It is important to be able to communicate effectively in a health or social care setting because a service user will not be able to take part in a discussion about their care or planning their future if they do not understand what is being said.

There are many barriers to communication.

Environmental barriers, e.g.:

- **Lighting** – someone who doesn't see very well will struggle to read written information in a dimly lit room.
- **Seating** – a person in a wheelchair or with dwarfism will be unable to communicate with a receptionist in a health and social care setting if the desk is too high for them to see over.
- **External noise** – someone with a hearing or speech impairment will not be able to communicate if they cannot receive or pass on information because there is too much noise.
- **Lack of space** – a person in a wheelchair will find it impossible to access a service if they cannot get into a room or across a room to a reception desk to communicate with a service provider.
- **Uneven surface or stairs** – wheelchair users or people with impaired mobility may not be able to access areas that have an uneven surface or stairs.

Physical barriers, e.g.:

- **Sensory deprivation** – when someone cannot receive or pass on information because they have an impairment to one or more of their senses, most commonly a visual or a hearing disability.
- **Physical and mental illness** – when someone is ill they may not be able to communicate as effectively as when they are well. Some long-term (chronic) illnesses such as Parkinson's disease or mental illness also affect an individual's ability to communicate.

Activity Environmental and physical barriers

Think about your own experience of health and social care settings, such as visits to the doctor, dentist or optician. Can you identify any barriers to communication? Discuss these with a partner and think about how they would make you feel if you were unwell or had a disability.

More factors

Language barriers, e.g.:

- **Foreign language** – someone speaking a different language or using sign language may not be able to make any sense of information they are being given by someone trying to help them.
- **Slang** – when a service user uses language that only a certain group of people use, misunderstanding or lack of understanding can occur. For instance someone saying they have a problem with their waterworks could mean their plumbing system, but also means a problem going to the toilet.
- **Jargon** – when a service provider uses technical language the service user may not understand. For example, the doctor may say that a patient needs bloods and an MRI scan. That can sound very frightening. It is better if the doctor explains that they need to take some blood to do some simple tests and then explains what a MRI scan is.

Social isolation, e.g.:

- **Lack of confidence** – a person may not have the confidence to ask a health or social care professional questions.
- **Intimidation** – when someone is intimidated by someone else, they won't be able to concentrate so will not be able to hear or understand what people are saying to them. They will also be reluctant to ask questions.
- **Following abuse** – abuse can cause someone to become withdrawn and unable to concentrate or communicate.
- **Trauma** – can cause distress and an inability to listen properly and so a person may misinterpret or not understand what is said.

> ### Key terms
>
> **Jargon** – technical words used by a professional person as a short way of saying things. These can be hard for non-professionals to understand.
>
> **Slang** – the use of informal words and expressions that are not considered standard in the speaker's dialect or language.
>
> **Social isolation** – when people live without regular contact with other people, especially family and friends.

Activity — Role play

1 Other barriers to communication include differing humour, sarcasm, inappropriate behaviour and aggression. In a group, discuss how each of these in turn would cause problems in a health and social care setting of your choice.

2 Pick one of these and role-play a situation in which it would be a barrier to communication if the person behaving like this was (i) a physiotherapist helping someone become more mobile after injuries in a road traffic accident, and (ii) a male patient being treated by a female nurse.

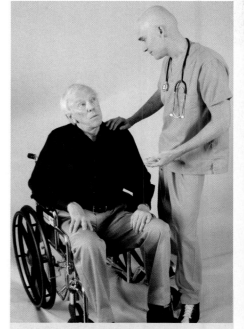

Standing over someone makes them feel uncomfortable and so less able to concentrate on what is being said.

Overcoming barriers to communication (1)

Introduction

In this topic you will learn about the effects of barriers to communication and why it is vital to overcome these barriers if people are to receive the care they need. You will also explore some of the ways to overcome these barriers.

◤ Effects of barriers

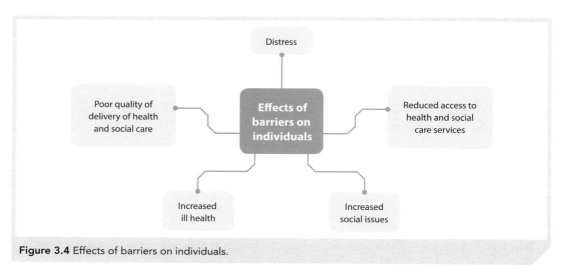

Figure 3.4 Effects of barriers on individuals.

Activity   Dealing with Down's Syndrome

1 Craig is a16-year-old young man who has Down's Syndrome. He lives at home with his parents who love him very much and has just left school to go to college. Do some research into how this change will affect his life and write a case study to describe the young man and his life.

2 Decide which barriers to communication are likely to apply to Craig.

3 Look at the effects of barriers to communication on individuals shown in Figure 3.4 above. Explain what the effects are likely to be on Craig.

4 How do you think this will change as Craig gets older and wants to become more independent?

5 How do you think these barriers could be reduced and maybe overcome?

◤ Overcoming barriers

Preferred method of communication

Service providers need to understand the preferences of the people they are supporting. For example, someone who is hearing-impaired may prefer to use Makaton rather than British Sign Language because that is what they are most familiar with.

Preferred language

It is important to find out what a service user's preferred language is for written and verbal communication. Most leaflets produced by public bodies, such as the NHS, are now written in a variety of languages so that people who do not speak English can access the information. If there is a member of staff who speaks the preferred language of a service user they can be asked to help translate or interpret, or a professional translator or interpreter can be employed.

Adaptations to the physical environment

- Changes to seating – chairs that enable the service user to be at the same level as the service provider, or vice versa, can help the service user feel less intimidated and more able to access the information needed.
- Changes to lighting – improving lighting can help those with sight impairments read information, such as directions.
- Soundproofing of rooms/windows – reducing background noise can help those with hearing impairments.
- Other changes – these might be installing lifts with a voice giving information, such as when the doors are opening and closing and which floor the lift is currently on. Other vital adaptations are adding ramps, lowering reception desks and putting signs lower down on walls for people with physical disabilities, so that they can access the people and information they need.

What potential barriers to communication can you identify in this waiting room and how can they be overcome?

| Activity | Effective non-verbal communication |

Look back at the two pages on effective non-verbal communication earlier in this unit. Explain how using positive posture, facial expressions and appropriate gestures can help overcome barriers to communication for a service user who (i) has learning difficulties, (ii) has recently arrived in the UK and can't speak English very well, and (iii) is annoyed.

Overcoming barriers to communication (2)

Benefits to individuals when barriers are removed

Raised levels of self-esteem

If people can understand what is being said by service providers they will be able to take part in planning their own care or future, which will make them feel valued and in control. This will result in increased **self-esteem**.

Reducing frustration

When a service user cannot access the information they need they become frustrated and distressed and less likely to understand what is being said to them. This is likely to cause stress symptoms, such as raised blood pressure and irritability. Reducing frustration by reducing or removing barriers to communication will enable service users to be calmer and more capable of accessing the information they need.

Activity Removing barriers to communication

Draw up a mind map to show the benefits to individuals when barriers are removed. Each branch should show one benefit. Create further branches from each benefit to show key words which sum up how this benefit helps the service user. You could use the spider diagram in Figure 3.4 and the information above to help you.

Case study

Communication barriers can also frustrate care givers. Verinda works for a charity that supports victims of road accidents. She works from home and becomes very frustrated on a regular basis by having to fill in a huge online form every time she deals with a client. The charity is only small so cannot afford to pay someone to update its systems but Verinda feels that the work done by the charity could be even more valuable if done more efficiently. Verinda doesn't feel she can ring up her boss and tell her how she feels because her boss lives in Canada, so she doesn't see her often and doesn't know her very well. She also doesn't trust herself not to lose her temper. Verinda has to hide this frustration when she is answering the phone to clients.

1 How do you think Verinda's frustration might affect her work?
2 How do you think Verinda can deal with this problem?
3 Role-play the conversation she could have with her boss on the phone about this, firstly where she lets her frustration show and loses her temper, and secondly where she is polite and manages to hide her frustration. What might be the possible consequences of each of these phone calls?

Using the tasks and questions on this page you will check what you have learned so far.

Assessment activity 3.2   2B.P3 | 2B.P4 | 2B.M2 | 2B.D2

In your role as a trainee early years worker at a nursery in a big town, you are producing information to help the nursery manager get some funding from the local council. She has now asked you to design a PowerPoint presentation with accompanying handout notes on the possible barriers to communication at the nursery and how the staff have worked to overcome them. She tells you that when she first took over as manager the nursery had:

- cluttered corridors so parents couldn't get close to notices pinned on walls
- noticeboards with cracked and dirty plastic covering them
- posters and notices that were old and fading
- no double glazing, curtains or carpets
- single light bulbs hanging from the centre of each ceiling covered with a cloth lampshade
- grubby windows
- very few signs in the corridor to show where different rooms were, how to find her office or where the toilets were
- a high old-fashioned reception desk
- no one who spoke any language other than English and no one had done any research into where to contact an interpreter or translator if needed
- older staff who had had very little additional training in issues such as communication skills since joining the staff many years before.

All these issues have now been addressed and the barriers they caused greatly reduced.

Your pack should include a case study about how effectively the nursery has managed to overcome barriers to communication with one of the children with learning difficulties.

Just checking

1. What do we mean by the expression 'barriers to communication'?
2. Why is it important for people who work in health and social care to understand barriers to communication?
3. Identify three physical barriers to communication and explain how they could be overcome.
4. Describe how an electronic device, such as a mobile phone, can help overcome barriers to communication.
5. How might emotional issues affect communications between a service user and a service provider?
6. Why is social isolation a barrier to communication? Explain your answer.
7. Describe three effects of barriers to communications on service users and explain how these can be reduced.

Developing communication skills (1)

Getting started

Working with a partner, tell each other about something you are proud of. Talk for about two minutes each. The person listening needs to listen carefully without making any notes and then repeat back what they have heard. How can you tell the person listening was concentrating?

Introduction

In this topic you will start to learn more skills for effective communication. These include body language, facial expression and eye contact. You have already looked at these briefly earlier in this unit.

Communicating with groups and individuals

Active listening

Listening to people involves more than just hearing what they say. To listen well you need to be able to hear the words being spoken, think what they mean and then think what to say in reply. You can also show that you are listening and what you think about what is being said by your body language, facial expressions and eye contact. Effective listening also means questioning anything you don't understand.

Yawning or looking at your notes or watch or looking round when someone is speaking will give the impression that you are bored by what is being said. This is not only very rude, but will also cause the person distress and negatively affect their self-esteem.

The process of active listening involves:

- allowing the person talking time to explain
- not interrupting
- giving encouragement by smiling, nodding and making remarks such as 'Really?' and 'Oh, yes?'
- asking questions for **clarification**, such as 'Can you explain that again, please?'
- showing **empathy** by making comments such as 'That must be so difficult for you.'
- looking interested by maintaining eye contact and not looking at anything else
- not being distracted by anything else – switch your mobile off
- summarising to check you have understood by repeating what has been said, saying for example, 'So what you mean is . . .'

Use of appropriate language

It is important to adjust your language to match the situation you are in and who you are talking to. People usually do this without even realising it, unconsciously changing their speech depending on who they are speaking to. For example, when speaking to a family member, they will be less formal than if they are ringing up the doctor for an appointment.

Key terms

Clarification – making something clear and understandable.

Empathy – imagining yourself in someone else's position in order to share and understand their emotions.

How can you tell that the people in the photo are interested and listening very carefully to each other?

Tone of voice

It is not just what you say but the way you say it that is important. If you talk to someone in a loud voice, with a fixed tone, the person will think that you are either angry with them or treating them as though they are less intelligent than you. It is important to speak calmly and quietly with a varying tone so the other person perceives that you are being friendly and kind and are interested in what they are saying.

| Activity | Improving communication skills |

Work with another member of your group and each sketch a few simple pictures, such as a house drawn as a child would draw it, or a Union flag, without the other one seeing what is being drawn.

Sit back to back, each with a pencil and piece of paper. Take it in turns to describe one of your sketches to the other person while they try to draw it as accurately as possible. You cannot use words that describe shapes, and must just talk about straight or curved lines at certain angles and starting at certain points on the page.

If the person drawing the picture draws it quite accurately, it means that one person has communicated well verbally while the other has listened carefully.

If the drawing is nothing like what it should be, discuss why you think this is.

Do this several times to practise and improve your communication skills.

Pace of speech

If you speak really quickly and excitedly, the person listening to you will not be able to make out everything you say. Similarly, if you speak very slowly, with lots of hesitation umms and errs, it makes it harder for people to concentrate on what you are saying. If you speak at a steady pace, however, you will be able to deliver your message more clearly and the other person will be able to hear every word you say.

Developing communication skills (2)

Proximity

The space around a person is called their personal space. In a formal situation, such as a doctor talking to a patient, the doctor does not sit close enough to the patient to invade their personal space, unless the doctor is going to examine the patient, in which case the doctor should explain in advance what they are planning to do so the patient is prepared. In an informal situation, people who are family, friends or intimate with each other will often sit closer to each other. You tend to stand or sit so you are eye-to-eye with someone if you are in a formal or aggressive situation, but sit at an angle in a more relaxed, friendly and less formal situation.

Other useful verbal skills

- Paraphrasing means repeating something a person has just said in a different way to make sure you have understood. For example, if someone says to you 'I have been feeling achy all over since Friday', you could paraphrase this by saying 'So you have had flu-like symptoms for five days now.'

- Closed questions are questions that can be answered with either a single word or short phrases, for example, 'Have you been sick today?' is likely to be answered by either 'yes' or 'no.' They are useful as an opening or closing question in a discussion, are easy and quick to answer and provide some facts quickly. A doctor might ask, 'So you want to see about having a knee replacement?' at the start of a consultation and finish by saying 'So is that your final decision?'

- Open questions are those that require a longer answer and give control of the conversation to the person you are asking, for example, 'Can you tell me where the pain is exactly and how it affects you?' An open question asks the person to think and reflect, and give opinions and feelings. They are useful to follow up a closed question, to find out more information, to help someone face their problems and to show concern for them.

How can this nurse use communication effectively to make the patient feel comfortable?

Case study

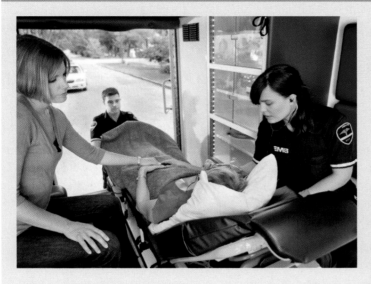

An adventure in France

Liz and Mike were enjoying their stay in France with Mike's daughter Sarah, a fluent French speaker. On their last day Liz was taken ill and passed out. Sarah called an ambulance but the paramedics only spoke very limited English so Sarah had to translate. Liz and Mike struggled to follow any of the conversation. The paramedics said Liz needed to be taken to the hospital, so Mike and Sarah followed the ambulance in Sarah's car.

In the ambulance Liz found herself lying flat on her back on a stretcher with a male paramedic sitting beside her, who kept trying to speak to her in French. During the journey she tried to communicate that she was going to be sick, using gestures and miming actions in order to communicate. At the hospital she was left on a trolley for over six hours in a long narrow corridor, lined with other sick people on trolleys, with no notices up explaining the system and no natural light. Sarah and Mike had to stand by her trolley. She was finally seen by three doctors, who didn't speak any English. Sarah spoke to them

but was then asked to leave the room while tests were carried out. Liz struggled to tell the doctors about her other medication and that she was allergic to penicillin. She was then left in the corridor again to wait for the test results. At 3 am Liz was admitted to the hospital so Sarah and Mike were sent home.

The next day another doctor with a little English came to examine Liz and decided that she was not to eat for at least two more days so she could have a full body scan. The nurses were all very kind, putting together the few English words they knew.

Sarah and Mike visited her for two hours each afternoon but otherwise Liz was on her own in a room.

Liz was finally diagnosed as having a swollen pancreas and told that her blood tests were returning to normal due to the fasting. She was finally allowed to eat again after three days but only dairy products. The next day, after breakfast of yoghurt and milk, she was finally discharged and allowed to fly home.

1 How do you think Liz felt when the paramedics couldn't speak any English?

2 How do you think the paramedics felt when they realised they had a patient who spoke very little French?

3 What were the barriers to communication during the long wait in the hospital corridor?

4 How could these have been minimised? How will they have affected Liz?

5 What were the barriers to communication once Liz had been admitted to a hospital bed?

6 How could these have been minimised? How will they have affected Liz?

7 How did the staff try to improve their communication with Liz?

Effectiveness of communication

Introduction

In this topic you will learn that it is important for health and social care workers to reflect on how effective their communication is as well as the importance of being able to communicate well using the written word. You will then have a chance to check your understanding of the work you have done recently.

Reflecting on skills

It is important to be able to select and demonstrate appropriate communication skills to use in different health and social care settings and for different service users. You should reflect on your communication skills so you know what skills you already have and use effectively. You can then work on improving those you use less well. It is also important to be able to make constructive recommendations for improvement to your friends.

This is also true of health and social care workers as it improves the effectiveness of communication. Remember that by communicating effectively, service users understand and agree to the care they are receiving, and service providers can perform their roles effectively, work cooperatively with each other and build supportive relationships with service users.

▶ Can you read that?

Written communication is central to the work of any person providing a service in a health and social care environment when keeping records and writing reports. Different types of communication need different styles of writing and different ways of presenting information but all require **literacy skills**. Meaning has to be clear and writing needs to be well structured and legible, with grammar, spelling and punctuation used correctly. A more formal style of writing and language is needed when recording information about a patient.

Key terms

Literacy skills – abilities required to speak, read and write clearly, correctly and accurately.

Activity   Written communications

1 In the first column of a table, make a list of all the different forms of writing a health and social care professional might use in a day. In the next column write down by each form as many uses for that type of written communication as you can think of. When your partner has also done this activity share your ideas to see if you can find any more.

2 Reflect on your own verbal, non-verbal and written communication. For each area decide what you do well, what you do less well and what you are going to do to improve those you do less well. Be totally honest with yourself.

3 Write an action plan for the improvements, in the form of a table which has columns for (i) each improvement to be made, (ii) the date it will be made by, (iii) what you need to help you do this, and (iv) notes, so you can record your progress towards making each improvement.

continued

Activity *continued*   Example template for action plan

Improvement to be made	Date it will be made by	What you need to help you	Notes

Assessment activity 3.3   *English*   2C.P5 | 2C.M3 | 2C.D3

1 You are going to role-play a conversation between yourself and a partner, where you are the trainee nursery nurse and your partner is the nursery manager. The conversation should be a discussion based on the training materials you produced in Assessment activity 3.1 and the PowerPoint you designed in Assessment activity 3.2.

2 Practise this conversation until you are satisfied that you are using your communication skills as well as you can.

3 Your teacher should have a video camera available so the conversation can be recorded to allow you to peer-assess and self-assess the conversation afterwards.

4 Repeat this process but this time swap roles.

5 Then combine with another pair in your class. This time carry out a group discussion comparing the best points of the four sets of training materials. Be honest, but be careful to only say positive things so that no one gets offended.

6 Video the group discussion and again peer-assess and self-assess everyone's communication skills.

7 Now watch your own performance in both interactions again and in a written report (i) identify and write down what communication skills you used, (ii) describe their effects, (iii) explain how effective they were, and (iv) make recommendations for how you can further improve your own communication skills.

Just checking

1 What do we mean by the expression 'active listening'?

2 Identify three active listening techniques and explain how they can be used effectively with a person who is distressed.

3 How can speaking too slowly and with lots of hesitation affect communication?

4 Why are clarifying and repeating useful techniques in verbal communication? What are the similarities and differences between the two techniques?

Introduction

How do you know the difference between right and wrong? Have you ever wondered why people hold the beliefs and attitudes they do, or how an individual's relationships and social factors, such as lifestyle or education, affect their health and wellbeing? If everyone did exactly what they wanted in this world, life would be chaotic. Fortunately, this is not the case because social influences, such as our families and our community, provide us with expectations and behaviours to conform to within our society. This is called socialisation.

In this unit you will find out more about how we learn acceptable behaviour from our parents or carers and the rest of our families and how we learn social rules from those in the wider community, for example teachers and work colleagues. You will also learn how these different forms of socialisation affect our health and wellbeing.

You will develop an understanding of the effects of a range of relationships and social factors on our health and wellbeing. This understanding is important in determining the types of care and support required by individuals, and allows health and social care professionals to plan and deliver care to meet the needs of service users.

Assessment: You will be assessed by a series of assignments set by your teacher/tutor.

Learning aims

In this unit you will:

A explore the effects of socialisation on the health and wellbeing of individuals

B understand the influences that relationships have on the health and wellbeing of individuals

C investigate the effects of social factors on the health and wellbeing of individuals.

> It's important not to judge people. When a young person comes into the clinic who is morbidly obese, it is easy to think they are stupid for getting in such a state, but often it is because their parents have encouraged them to eat junk food and haven't taught them about a healthy diet because they didn't know either.
>
> Nathan, *19-year-old student dietician*

Social Influences on Health and Wellbeing

4

BTEC
Assessment Zone

This table shows what you must do in order to achieve a **Pass**, **Merit** or **Distinction** grade, and where you can find activities in this book to help you.

Assessment criteria			
Level 1	Level 2 Pass	Level 2 Merit	Level 2 Distinction
Learning aim A: Explore the effects of socialisation on the health and wellbeing of individuals			
1A.1 Identify agents involved in the primary and secondary socialisation processes.	**2A.P1** Explain the influence of agents of primary and secondary socialisation. **Assessment activity 4.1** See page 87.	**2A.M1** Explain the effects of primary and secondary socialisation on the health and wellbeing of individuals, with reference to relevant examples. **Assessment activity 4.1** See page 87.	**2A.D1** Evaluate the impact of primary and secondary socialisation on the health and wellbeing of individuals, with reference to relevant examples. **Assessment activity 4.1** See page 87.
1A.2 Outline the main effects of socialisation on the health and wellbeing of individuals.	**2A.P2** Describe the effects of socialisation on the health and wellbeing of individuals. **Assessment activity 4.1** See page 87.		
Learning aim B: Understand the influences that relationships have on the health and wellbeing of individuals			
1B.3 Outline the different types of relationships that have an impact on the health and wellbeing of individuals.	**2B.P3** Describe the influences that different types of relationships have on the health and wellbeing of individuals. **Assessment activity 4.2** See page 92.	**2B.M2** Explain the influences that different types of relationships have on the health and wellbeing of individuals. **Assessment activity 4.2** See page 92.	**2B.D2** Compare the potential positive and negative influences of different relationships on the health and wellbeing of individuals. **Assessment activity 4.2** See page 92.
Learning aim C: Investigate the effects of social factors on the health and wellbeing of individuals			
1C.4 Identify the effects of social factors on the health choices of individuals.	**2C.P4** Describe how social factors can affect the health and wellbeing of individuals **Assessment activity 4.3** See page 99.	**2C.M3** Explain how social factors can affect the health and wellbeing of individuals, with reference to relevant examples. **Assessment activity 4.3** See page 99.	**2C.D3** Evaluate the link between social factors and the health and wellbeing of individuals, and the impact on health and wellbeing, with reference to relevant examples. **Assessment activity 4.3** See page 99.

How you will be assessed

This unit will be assessed by either one, or a series of smaller, internally assessed tasks. You will be expected to show an understanding of socialisation in the context of health and social care sectors. The tasks will be based on a case study in which you are working in a local health or social care organisation where the staff want to reduce the number of preventable health problems. For example, your manager asks you to produce materials that can be used to help raise awareness of the positive and negative effects of social influences on people's health and wellbeing. You will produce a series of leaflets featuring fictional characters designed to show parents potential influences on their children as they grow up, and the impact these will have on health and wellbeing.

Your assessment could be in the form of leaflets accompanied by:

- a written report/article

or

- a verbal presentation with presentation notes and slides, and a signed observation record/witness testimony.

Whichever one you choose, you should look at one or a few case studies which highlight:

- the effects of primary and secondary socialisation on health and wellbeing
- the influences of relationships on health and wellbeing
- the effects of social factors on health and wellbeing.

Socialisation

Getting started ▶▶

How do you know the difference between right and wrong? Who taught you this? How did you learn it? How do you know how to behave?

Think about these questions and then compare your thoughts with a partner.

Key terms

Agent – a person who causes a change.

Accent – a way of pronouncing a language.

Dialect – a way of speaking found only in a certain area or among a certain group or class of people.

Introduction

Socialisation is the process of learning to understand the expected roles, values and normal behaviours that allow an individual to become a part of a social group or culture and society in general. In this section, you will learn about primary and secondary socialisation, which groups of people are its agents, and the influence of these agents on speech, beliefs and values. It is important that you understand the difference between primary and secondary socialisation.

◤ Primary socialisation

Primary socialisation usually happens within the family in the first five years of a child's life. Children learn about acceptable ways of behaving, mainly from family members and especially parents, before they reach school age. The **agents** of primary socialisation are:

- close family, e.g. parents, siblings, grandparents
- other carers, e.g. childminders and babysitters.

Speech

Children learn to speak from their families and other carers. An unborn baby tunes into the sound of the mother's voice while still in the womb, and after birth is able to recognise that voice among others. From the moment a baby is born, they are learning the rules of language and how others use it to communicate. A baby's first cry is followed by the absorption of sounds, tones and words from those around them, which will later shape the way they speak. Children usually learn to talk during the first two years of life; they learn what words sound like and how sentences are structured by listening to others speak. Research shows that children whose parents speak or read to them a lot when they are babies have much higher IQs and richer vocabularies than other children. Children also learn **accents** and **dialects** at an early age from their families and carers.

Beliefs

Beliefs are strongly held opinions and assumptions about the world that determine how an individual sees life. Have you ever thought carefully about what you believe in? Most people don't reflect much on what they believe, but their beliefs still influence their everyday thoughts, feelings and actions.

These beliefs stem from our upbringing, events that happen in our lives and the influences of others. They grow from what we see, hear, experience, read and think about and they affect not only ourselves but the way we see other people.

What behaviour may this baby learn to copy from its mother?

Children adopt their beliefs in the first years of their lives from their family and others who look after them. If a child is taken to church from an early age, they are likely to grow up believing in God. We tend not to question our beliefs because we are certain about them and many of them stem from our childhood; however, they can change as we grow older and are influenced by a greater range of agents.

Values

Our values are things that we consider to be important, worthwhile and morally right. These may include equality, honesty, dignity, respect, perseverance and loyalty. Our values are individual and they affect us at a deep subconscious level. Every decision we make is based on our values and we may either use them for avoidance or for aspiration. We start to learn these at a very early age when our parents or other carers teach us what is right and wrong and how to be polite to other people.

Secondary socialisation

Secondary socialisation is usually as a result of what children experience outside the home. It takes place with other adults and children. The agents of secondary socialisation are shown in Figure 4.1.

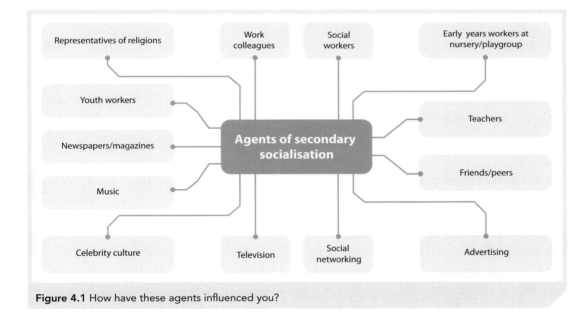

Figure 4.1 How have these agents influenced you?

Activity   Who has influenced you?

Think about the people or other factors that have influenced the way you behave and think. Think back as far as you can remember. Draw up a mind map showing each agent identified in Figure 4.1 and how they influenced you (you must be totally honest). Then decide who or what influenced you most: (1) during the first five years of your life, (2) during your time at primary school, and (3) during your time at secondary school.

Effects of socialisation (1)

Introduction

An effect of socialisation is the shaping of gender roles, for example the expectations of male and female behaviour. Another effect is the shaping of attitudes, such as the development of **tolerance** or **prejudice**.

Gender roles

A person's sex is determined genetically, but gender refers to the different expectations for male and female behaviour which start to be learned at an early age. Gender roles determine how males and females should think, speak, dress and behave in their interactions with others. Agents of primary socialisation, particularly parents, exert the greatest influence on the learning of gender roles, but secondary socialising agents teach and reinforce these roles throughout our lives.

Traditionally, mothers taught girls how to cook, clean, iron and sew, and fathers taught boys how to mend, build things and play ball games. In this way, the values of parents and society are passed from generation to generation. Even when parents make a determined effort not to reinforce this stereotypical behaviour, most children fall into these ways of behaving because of other influences around them. One example is toys. Many girls' toys are pink and involve nurturing or other stereotypical behaviours, such as dolls that need feeding and dressing, whereas boys' toys are rarely pink and are more often action figures or vehicles. This continues as we grow up, as there are assumptions made about financial responsibilities, housework, decision making and child rearing.

Gender **stereotyping** is often reinforced in the workplace, although this is less so than it used to be.

Key terms

Tolerance – the capacity to recognise and respect the beliefs or practices of others, even if we don't agree with them.

Prejudice – an unreasonable feeling against a person or group of people.

Stereotyping – thinking a group of people will all have the same attribute, for example, that all older people are deaf and forgetful.

Activity Gender roles

1 On a large sheet of paper, write down expressions which adults use to children based on gender roles, e.g. 'Act like a man/woman'. On another sheet, write down words which are often used to describe males and females, e.g. 'handsome' or 'pretty', 'weak' or 'strong'.

2 Invite all members of the group to add their ideas and then discuss what this shows.

3 Traditionally males were expected not to show emotion in public; for example, they were supposed never to be seen to cry. Nowadays, males are more likely to show their emotions. Discuss whether you think this is a good or bad thing.

4 Think about your local medical centre and the roles of males and females within it. What sex do the receptionists tend to be? What sex are most of the nurses and doctors?

Shaping of attitudes

Attitude is the way a person views (or behaves towards) something or someone, often in an evaluative way. Our attitudes are central to who we are. Children watch their parents carefully and instinctively imitate their behaviour. Therefore, if parents are always bad-tempered, irritable and selfish, their children will grow up with a tendency to be the same. If parents always say 'please' and 'thank you', and praise their children for doing the same, the children are likely to have good manners.

Activity — Attitudes

Winston Churchill was a British politician, author and Prime Minister during the Second World War and lived between 1874 and 1965. One of his many famous quotes was that 'attitude is a little thing that makes a big difference'.

1 What do you think he meant by this?

2 Have you ever seen or been involved in a situation where someone displayed a negative attitude, for example being disrespectful to a teacher or the police? How did this attitude affect the way the people involved communicated with each other?

3 Think of another situation where someone's attitude affected a situation. Describe the situation to a partner and explain how the person could have made the outcome more positive.

4 Why do you think it is important for a person working in a health or social care context to have a positive and pleasant attitude?

Tolerance and prejudice

Someone may have a prejudice against a group of people for reasons such as age, gender, race, ethnicity, class, religion, sexual orientation, ability, health, disability or appearance. They might then treat them differently. Other people are more tolerant, accepting that a group of people has a right to be different from them if they are not causing anyone else any harm. This behaviour is learned early in life from families, and reinforced by others as we get older. Therefore, if children hear parents referring to someone who is not very clever in a derogatory way, they are likely to use the same language in the same situation and cause offence. If parents always speak about other groups of people in a positive and respectful manner, children are more likely to grow up to be tolerant adults.

Can you find any more of Winston Churchill's quotes about attitudes?

Effects of socialisation (2)

Getting started ▶▶

Older people sometimes make comments about young people not having the high moral standards that they had when they were their age, lacking respect for adults and lacking the determination to work hard to succeed. Why do you think they believe this? Are they right?

Link

This topic links to Unit 7: Equality and Diversity in Health and Socal Care.

Shaping of moral choices

Parents, or other carers, have the greatest influence on a child's life, as children learn by example. When children experience interactions inside and outside the home in which they feel safe and cared for and where anger and hostility are not present, they develop a strong sense of self which develops into a strong moral base. When they see or experience something such as violence that is different from their normal way of living, they instinctively know that it is wrong. Parents who talk about the basis of their moral principles and the expectations and rewards of following those principles usually succeed in teaching their children to hold to the same level of morals as they have.

Secondary agents also play a large part in shaping moral attitudes. Role models, such as other adults, have an important role to play because children tend to look up to them and believe what they say and do is correct. If any adult they know behaves inappropriately, children may think that is acceptable behaviour. Children need guidance to choose suitable role models. They also need the chance to interact with a range of adults and other children, of all ages. In learning how to get along with others, and learning the social conventions which help them fit in, their interactions reinforce or challenge a child's preconceived ideas about what is morally acceptable.

Religious and secular beliefs

Children are influenced by the culture that surrounds them, so if they are brought up in a culture that has strong religious or secular beliefs they will tend to accept those beliefs as their own.

Attitude to authority

Our attitude to authority is affected very much by the attitude of our parents or carers towards people in authority, which is often based on their experience of authority when they were young and which they subconsciously pass on to us. Parents are the first authority figures we have contact with and if they teach us to behave by using fear, then we will grow up to fear or resent other people in authority.

If parents tell their children that the police are there to help them and if they don't do anything wrong they won't punish them, they will grow up respecting the police. On the other hand, if parents say that the police are corrupt and call them derogatory names, children are likely to grow up with the same attitude.

Development of social norms and values

A social norm is behaviour that is expected by a family, social or ethnic grouping in any given situation and is based on the values of that grouping. Children develop views of what is right and wrong from primary agents and these are reinforced by secondary agents of socialisation. If parents do not provide clear boundaries, the child is unsure how to behave and as they grow older they will look to other people to provide a role model. This may be a good role model, but may equally be someone who shows them the wrong behaviour to model their own behaviour on.

In teenage years the influence of friends or a peer group becomes very important. If it is the norm within a group to speak to authority figures rudely, swear, smoke, drink or take part in criminal activities, the group members will feel pressured to act in this way to be accepted.

Case study

From: Jay Patel (jay@rowshamyouth.org.uk)
Sent: 18 July 2012 15:19
To: Carol Charnley (manager@rowshamyouth.org.uk)
Subject: Kelly Perreira

Hi Carol

I thought I should let you know about a conversation I had with Kelly Perreira this evening.

Kelly is 15 and attends our centre regularly. She was very upset when she came in this evening as she was arrested last night for drunk and disorderly behaviour and narrowly avoided being charged with shoplifting.

Kelly missed school yesterday and said this is because she is being bullied about her weight by girls in her year. She now hangs around with a group of older boys and was with them last night. Kelly says her parents are very angry with her, but don't understand how unhappy she is.

I will be away next week, so I'd be grateful if you could keep an eye out for Kelly.

Jay

1 How are primary and secondary agents of socialisation influencing Kelly?
2 What effects are these having on Kelly's health and wellbeing?

Influence on lifestyle choices

Introduction

Socialisation influences our lifestyle choices. Some of the lifestyle choices we make are shown in Figure 4.2. Although we will only look at one of these, you should understand how socialisation affects all these and other lifestyle choices.

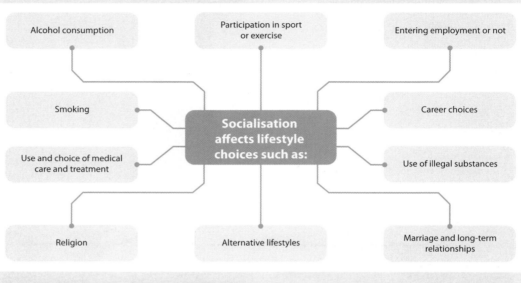

Figure 4.2 What decisions will you make, and why?

◤ Smoking

As we are strongly influenced by our parents and other people we look up to, such as our peers and figures in the media, we have a tendency to copy their behaviour. Children whose parents smoke are approximately twice as likely to start smoking compared with those with non-smoking parents. Most smokers start in their teens, with girls more likely to smoke than boys. Peer pressure and the desire to create a certain image are strong influences. There is an almost immediate effect on the brain with the first cigarette smoked, so teenagers continue smoking to get this reward. Smoking can play an important role in friendships: offering a cigarette or light can be an ice-breaker and huddling together outside, maybe in some hidden place at school or college or outside at a workplace, creates a bond.

We are also influenced by the media. Actors smoking on television and in films can suggest a link with glamour, sex and risk-taking. Although adverts for smoking products are no longer allowed on television, the tobacco industry sponsors risky sports, such as motor racing. Deciding to give up can imply a criticism of others in the group, and so can cause a rift. Later in life smokers learn to associate having a cigarette with other activities, such as having a drink break at work.

Smoking is a biological addiction and a psychological habit, so smokers immediately have withdrawal symptoms when they give up. Smokers therefore keep smoking to avoid these symptoms. Awareness of the damage to a smoker's health takes years to build up, so it is easy to think that there is plenty of time to give up later.

the dangers of smoking around children.

Explore the effects of socialisation on the health and wellbeing of individuals

Below are some questions to test what you have learned. You can then complete a practice assessment assignment.

Did you know?

A study by the World Health Organization showed that the 11 to 15-year-olds who were most likely to smoke were lonely, had difficulty talking to parents, had problems at school and had started to drink alcohol.

Just checking

1 What is meant by primary socialisation?

2 Name three groups of people who are agents of primary socialisation.

3 What is meant by secondary socialisation?

4 List three agents of secondary socialisation.

5 How do (i) primary agents, and (ii) secondary agents shape our gender roles?

6 Use an example to explain how we develop tolerance of, or prejudice towards, a group of people we see as different from ourselves.

7 How do we develop our attitude towards authority? How are we likely to react later in life towards authority figures if we have (i) a positive attitude towards authority, and (ii) a negative attitude towards authority? Use examples of certain groups of authority figures to explain your answer.

8 Give an example of what is meant by a social norm and how we develop it.

9 How do agents of socialisation affect our choice to (i) enter employment or not, (ii) use drugs, and (iii) use medical care and treatment?

Assessment activity 4.1

2A.P1 | 2A.P2 | 2A.M1 | 2A.D1

You are a youth worker at a youth centre in a big town. Staff at the local healthcare centre ask you to help raise awareness of the effects of primary and secondary socialisation on the health and wellbeing of young people.

They ask you to produce a series of leaflets featuring fictional characters and relevant examples to show parents and their children the potential influence of primary and secondary socialisation on the values, attitudes, behaviour and lifestyle choices of young people, and the ways in which these could affect their health and wellbeing.

Your leaflets should compare and evaluate the importance of the influence of different agents of socialisation in terms of shaping of gender roles, attitudes, the development of social norms and values, and the influence of lifestyle choices. Your teacher/tutor will provide you with a case study on which to base your leaflets.

Tips

To evaluate the impact of socialisation, you need to make a judgement on what is most important, backing up your arguments with at least three detailed examples. You should decide whether primary or secondary socialisation was more influential on the person studied, or which form of socialisation had a largely positive or negative effect.

Influences of relationships on individuals

Introduction

Different types of relationships, and changes in those relationships, influence the health and wellbeing of individuals.

Different types of relationships

Family

Almost everyone will live in a **family** unit at some stage in their life. There are various different types of family.

What are the advantages of a family unit?

- *Extended:* this type of family consists of at least three generations of one family, i.e. grandparents, parents and children, who live either together or close to each other and have very regular contact.
- *Nuclear:* this family consists of two parents living together with their children.
- *Reconstituted:* in this type of family a parent who already has children from a previous relationship sets up home with another person who may or may not also be a parent, so the children have a step-parent. The couple may go on to have children together.
- *Single parent:* this family is made up of one parent and that parent's child or children. This comes about because the parent has been widowed, divorced or separated, or the parent never married or lived with the parent of their children.

1 Your class should divide into four groups. Each group takes one type of family and draws up a table to show its advantages and disadvantages. Be sensitive to the fact that there are likely to be members of the class from all four types of family.

2 Share your ideas with the other groups and add any other points that arise in the class discussion.

3 Each group should record how being a member of that type of family affects (i) the children's, and (ii) the parents' health and wellbeing by writing both positive and negative points under the PIES headings.

4 If you have time, research what percentage of families in the UK fall into each category of family.

Working

Working relationships also vary, but are either formal or informal. Formal relationships are with those who manage us, and any discussions are formal and professional. Examples are between a worker and their **line manger** or between a teacher and learner. Informal relationships develop with those we work alongside (**colleagues**), who may become close friends or even our partners.

Working relationships affect our health and wellbeing. They affect us physically (P) by the level of stress they do or do not cause us, intellectually (I) as we learn new skills and information from work colleagues, emotionally (E) by how happy we are at work, and socially (S) by the opportunities we get to become involved with colleagues socially.

Social

We form social relationships with friends and fellow members of groups, religious or **secular**. Friendships play an important role in our lives as they provide us with someone to give us practical support and advice, take part in activities such as exercise and leisure pursuits with (P), learn with (I), share our feelings with (E) and spend time with (S). We tend to become friends with those we consider to be like ourselves, with similar values, attitudes and interests.

Intimate and sexual relationships

When these are happy successful relationships, they provide us with someone with whom we can have a satisfying physical relationship. Together we can take part in a range of activities which keep us physically active, also travel, and take part in leisure activities and events, such as quizzes, which keep us intellectually stimulated. We can share our feelings and problems, so meeting our emotional needs, and take up social opportunities, as well as maybe have a family and so meet more of our needs.

Remember

Don't forget to use PIES to track how we develop throughout our lives, as in the example saying how working relationships affect our health and wellbeing.

Key terms

Secular – something that has no connection to any religion or place of workship.

Influences of relationships on the health and wellbeing of individuals (1)

Introduction

Relationships have an effect on us when they change, for example in marriage, divorce, bereavement and leaving education.

Relationship changes

When any relationship changes, it affects us in positive and negative ways. Any such change affects our **self-esteem**, levels of stress and anxiety, and can lead to **dysfunction**. Marriage is generally a very positive and happy event, leading to a happy settled life with a partner. Divorce is generally a negative event; even though a person may decide it is what they want and feel relief that they will no longer be living in an unhappy situation, it may still bring negative feelings and other consequences.

Table 4.1 Contrasting effects of marriage and divorce on health and wellbeing.

Aspects of health and wellbeing	Marriage	Divorce
Physical	**Positive**: *Healthy sex life, someone to do activities with*	**Positive**: *May have more flexibility to choose food and exercise, rather than fitting in with another's choices*
	Negative: *May take on each others' bad habits of unhealthy eating or not exercising*	**Negative**: *May have less money, therefore affects diet, opportunities to exercise, general standard of living conditions*
Intellectual	Positive:	Positive:
	Negative:	Negative:
Emotional	Positive:	Positive:
	Negative:	Negative:
Social	Positive:	Positive:
	Negative:	Negative:

Key terms

Self-esteem – how much you like, accept and respect yourself as a person, how you value yourself.

Dysfunction – when the physical or emotional aspects of a relationship are not working as expected.

Activity   Relationship changes

In groups, consider the positive and negative effects of marriage and divorce. Complete Table 4.1 on which the full aspect has been started for you. Share your ideas with the rest of the class.

Self-esteem

A positive and happy change in a relationship makes us feel good about ourselves, and it helps us to like ourselves and believe that others like us too. We are more confident and feel more capable and attractive.

Levels of stress and anxiety

A change in a relationship which causes us to be upset or unsure of the future, such as bereavement, can raise our levels of stress and anxiety. This can lead to the effects shown in Figure 4.3 below.

A bereaved person suffers the physical effects of stress. These affect their intellectual needs as they will be distracted and lack concentration, their emotional needs as they will be unhappy, and their social needs as they will find it difficult to mix with others on their own.

Link

This topic links to Unit 1: Human Lifespan Development.

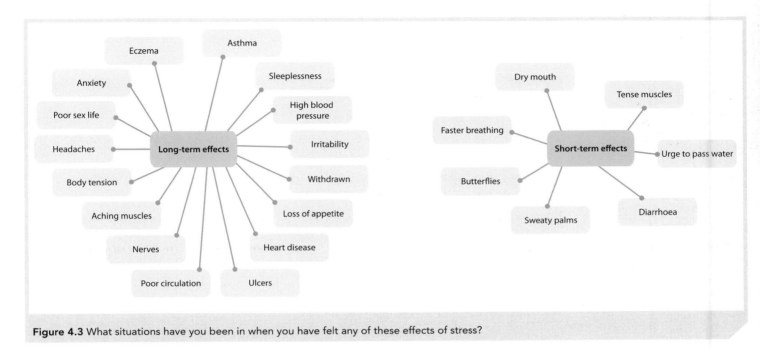

Figure 4.3 What situations have you been in when you have felt any of these effects of stress?

Dysfunction

A relationship change can lead to dysfunction, for example, when a couple marry and have a family but the relationship doesn't work out. In some cases this may be because one or both parents is addicted to substances such as alcohol or drugs, is suffering from an untreated mental illness, or is copying the behaviour of their own dysfunctional parents. This means that conflict, misbehaviour, and even abuse on the part of individual members starts to occur. Any major source of stress, such as moving house, unemployment and illness can cause existing conflicts affecting the children to become worse. Children who grow up with dysfunction may come to believe this behaviour is normal and can become dysfunctional parents themselves.

Dysfunction can lead to neglect of physical needs; the parents and children suffer from stress, poor diet, the effects of substances such as alcohol, and even abuse. This affects intellectual needs as it is very hard to concentrate on learning or using work skills in such a situation. It affects emotional needs as all concerned are unhappy, and social needs because there is no money to go out and if they do, a greater likelihood of a conflict arising.

Influences of relationships on the health and wellbeing of individuals (2)

Activity   Leaving education

Think about leaving education at the end of school, college or university. How will this affect a person's health and wellbeing? Draw up a table similar to Table 4.1, showing the effects on PIES. In pairs, compare your tables. Add any new ideas to your table.

Below are some questions to test what you have learned. You can then complete a practice assessment assignment.

Just checking

1 Name four different types of family.

2 How does being a single parent affect a person's health and wellbeing? Remember to include positive and negative points.

3 Give an example of (i) a formal working relationship, and (ii) an informal working relationship.

4 How does a negative relationship between an employee and their line manager affect (i) the line manager's health and wellbeing, and (ii) the employee's health and wellbeing?

5 Give an example of a social group, and explain what would make them likely to become a group.

6 How does having a successful intimate and sexual relationship help a person's health and wellbeing? Explain using PIES.

7 How does bereavement affect a person's self-esteem?

8 How does divorce contribute to a family's dysfunction? Explain your answer.

9 How does leaving education affect a person's levels of stress and anxiety?

10 How does marriage affect a person's health and wellbeing?

Assessment activity 4.2   2B.P3 | 2B.M2 | 2B.D2

As a youth worker at a youth centre in a big town, you have already produced a series of leaflets for the local healthcare centre to help raise awareness of the effects of primary and secondary socialisation on the health and wellbeing of young people.

The staff at the centre ask you to extend your leaflets to produce a report to show parents and their children the influence of different types of relationships, and the positive and negative ways these can influence their health and wellbeing.

Tips

When describing the influence of a range of relationships, which includes the influence of any changes in relationships, you should use evidence such as research from articles in the media or scientific and health-related reports, and give reasons to support the points you are making. Compare the likely negative and positive influences of the person's different relationships on their health and wellbeing.

WorkSpace

▶ **AMAN BALLI**

Youth Worker

I am a youth worker in a busy, big, town-based youth centre. I work in a team which includes other youth workers, one of whom is the manager, and a cleaner. We have regular contact with the police and social workers, and the Police Community Support Officers often drop in during the evening for a cup of tea (or a brew, as they call it!) and a chat with the young people who come here. We have one large open-plan room for the main activities. At one end is a pool table, and in one corner some video games, so people can sit on big bean bags on the floor and play games together. The other end of the room has easy chairs, books and magazines, so they can have some quiet time away from the games and pool table. One corner has a vending machine for snacks and a kitchenette so they can make themselves a hot drink.

My main task is to organise activities for those young people who want to take part, such as pool tournaments, card game evenings, gaming competitions, and occasional evening trips to the ice rink or somewhere similar when funds allow. The young people choose where they would like to go and help organise it, as this helps them to work together as a group and learn new interpersonal skills. I help keep accurate records on the attendance of the young people and any other necessary information, such as medical details and emergency contact details.

Think about it

1 Why are developing good relationships so important to Aman's job?

2 How is Aman likely to be able to help when young people have problems, such as changing relationships when a parent remarries?

3 What are your strengths when it comes to building effective relationships? And what are the areas that you would like to improve?

Social factors

Introduction

Social factors are connections with people that affect something else in our lives. There are various social factors that influence health and wellbeing. This topic looks at one of those factors, social class, in detail.

Figure 4.4 Which of these factors do you notice affecting your life?

Social class

Social class is a person's position in a **hierarchy** of groups within a society and this is determined by their occupation and income. The British system was traditionally divided into three layers: working class, middle class and upper class. The higher up the class system a person belonged, the more power and influence they had. There were more working-class people than middle-class, and more middle-class than upper-class. Upper-class people tended to be those with inherited **wealth**. The middle class included industrialists, professionals and business people. The working class included agricultural and factory workers, people who work with their hands.

Due to the ever-increasing variety of jobs, the class system has become more complicated over the years and since 2001 has been divided into eight classes, according to occupation. Even this is not totally clear. Someone who is, for example, a factory worker, might win the lottery and become a millionaire but this alone does not make them upper-class.

Occupation

Most people spend a large part of their adult lives working. This provides the **income** to buy the goods and services they need for themselves and their family. Jobs can be **manual**, which means they may be very physically demanding, tiring and sometimes can lead to injuries, or **non-manual**, which usually means sitting at a desk. Sometimes the latter can be stressful and the work may involve little exercise, leading to the type of lifestyle that is linked to high blood pressure and heart disease.

Income

Most people's money comes from the income they earn for the work they do. Some people can't work for reasons such as disability, illness or caring for someone else, and so claim benefits from the state. The level of income a person earns is mainly linked to the skills, education, qualifications and talents they have, how hard they work and their area of work.

Influence on health and wellbeing

Social class affects health and wellbeing; a person in a lower social class is likely to have fewer opportunities and therefore poorer **employment prospects** and a lower income than a person in a higher social class. This makes life more difficult, as people can find it hard to meet even their most basic needs. There are still a large number of people in the UK who live in **poverty**.

People higher up the social class system tend to live longer than those from working-class backgrounds. People who can afford to buy healthy foods are more likely to be physically healthy, and can exercise more (P). They can go to a variety of places and take part in more activities, so have more opportunities to learn (I). They will be less stressed about financial problems and less likely to have failing relationships, so they will be happier (E) and have more opportunities to meet new people and enjoy time with friends (S). However, although wealth may allow people to buy private education, get private healthcare and have more **material possessions** than others, it does not guarantee health and wellbeing. Wealthy people can still become ill or have accidents. They may work so hard for their wealth that they don't have time to spend it, or time with their families. This can cause stress and failing relationships.

Activity   Social factors

In pairs, choose one of the social factors (other than social class) shown in Figure 4.4. Produce a mind map showing how that factor influences (i) a person's health choices, and (ii) their health and wellbeing (now and in the long term), including levels of stress and anxiety.

Is money the key to happiness?

Effects of social factors on health choices

Getting started ▶▶

Reflect on your life so far. What health choices have been made for you by others? What health choices have you made yourself?

Introduction

Social factors affect health choices. These health choices include diet, smoking, living accommodation, use of recreational drugs, alcohol consumption, participation in sport or exercise, and seeking medical care. This topic looks at one of these choices, participation in sport or exercise, in detail.

Health-related choices

These are choices such as whether to pay for private healthcare, whether to take advantage of healthcare monitoring opportunities such as regular health checks with your doctor, optician and dentist, and how you choose to live your life, depending on a range of social and economic factors.

Some choices are in effect made for us, because although the UK is a welfare state with health and social care services provided for all, some people experience difficulty in accessing the services they need. This may be because they can't afford the costs of transport to a health provider, prescriptions, or dentist's or optician's fees. They may be in a rural location with no available transport to the services, or they may have a mobility problem or find travel uncomfortable, and therefore choose to stay away.

Participation in sport or exercise

All schools today teach children why it is important to take part in sport or exercise, so we are all aware of why we should do this. The social factors mentioned in the last section all affect our choice to exercise or not.

- *Physical benefits*: any kind of physical activity reduces the risk of developing many major illnesses and conditions which can lead to an early death, such as type 2 diabetes, heart disease, cancer, high blood pressure, osteoporosis and obesity. It also helps improve sleep, reduces stress, helps coordination and improves stamina, strength and suppleness.

Why is it important to teach children about exercise from an early age?

- *Intellectual benefits:* it is believed that exercise is linked to our brain function and improves our ability to learn and solve problems, memory and recovery after injury. Playing for a team can lead to travel so we learn more about our country and other cultures. While exercising or taking part in sport we are also learning new skills and rules.

- *Emotional benefits:* exercise is believed to release endorphins form the pituitary gland in the brain and this not only gives us a sense of wellbeing and happiness after taking exercise but also helps to suppress pain. Even if it is not due to endorphins, actually doing some exercise can make us feel as though we have done something good for ourselves and achieved something, as can doing well when we compete and succeed. Exercise reduces stress and relaxes us, giving us space and time to think about things away from the pressures of everyday life.

- *Social effects:* many people take part in exercise or sport with a group of people or in teams, which can lead to making new friends or making friendships closer and stronger through a shared interest. This is not only based on the shared activity but also on the after-exercise opportunities, such as going for a drink together.

Choosing not to participate in sport or exercise

By choosing not to participate, all the opportunities to receive the benefits mentioned are missed. Although some people have very little free time or money or company, there are simple exercises which can be done at a desk at work or sitting in front of the television, which are quick and don't cost anything. If embarrassment is a problem there are ways round that; many public swimming pools, for example, have women-only sessions for women who feel uncomfortable wearing a swimming costume in front of men, or who have cultural reasons for not swimming at the same time as men. Activities such as gardening are also very good exercise and provide all the benefits mentioned without having to move out of your own garden. A person can burn up to 300 calories doing one hour of moderately active gardening.

Other factors stopping us exercising

Others factors prevent us from exercising. If we eat the wrong foods and become obese, it is harder to make the decision to exercise and harder work to start with. Smoking affects our lung capacity and leads to quickly becoming breathless when exercising, so making us more ready to give up. If we have very little money to buy clothes to wear for exercise, or poor living conditions where it is hard to wash and dry clothes, it also puts us off. The use of recreational drugs or drinking too much alcohol can also make us feel bad, as well as make us unfit, so again we are put off bothering to even think about exercise.

Activity	Health choices

The class should divide into small groups, each taking one of the health choices mentioned at the start of this topic. Discuss how the social factors identified in Figure 4.4 affects the health choice your group has chosen. Produce a PowerPoint presentation to show to the rest of the class.

Effects of social factors on the health and wellbeing of individuals

Introduction

In this topic you will learn how social factors affect our self-esteem and access to health and social care services.

Table 4.2 How social factors affect self-esteem and access to health and social care services.

Factor	Self-esteem	Access to health and social care services
Income	More positive if fewer money worries	More income, more able to pay for transport
Education	Better educated, feel better about self	More likely to realise the importance of accessing services
Occupation	Higher status job, feel good about self	All have access, some jobs make it easier to get time to access services
Social class	Higher social class, more positive and confident	More likely to access services if higher social class
Wealth	More wealth, often feel better, fewer money worries	Can afford private healthcare, including dental and eye care
Values and behaviours	Positive values and behaviours, feel better about self	Value self more so more likely to access services as soon as needed
Family	Loving supportive family, make you feel valued and worthy	Supportive and caring, will make sure you access services you need
Peers	Kind, supportive and caring, make you feel you belong and like yourself	Go with you or persuade you to go to services if need to
Media	Good stories about people like us, feel-good factor	Health promotion campaigns and reports raise our awareness of services
Living conditions	Comfortable, warm, pleasant home, feels good, not ashamed when peers visit	Good, less likely to need services, less reluctant to resent people providing services
Gender	Feel good if happy with gender role	Females likely to access services earlier than males
Culture	Depends on regard held in local community, if not resented or treated differently, feels good	Services able to address cultural issues as UK is multicultural; may need to raise awareness of this in certain cultures and areas

Below are some questions to test what you have learned. You can then complete a practice assessment assignment.

Activity	Effects of social factors on health and wellbeing

Choose three of the social factors in Table 4.2 and write a detailed report on how each factor affects (i) self-esteem, and (ii) access to health and social care services. Include up-to-date statistics and both positive and negative points. Finish with a conclusion which you will share with the rest of the class.

Just checking

1. Name three social factors and explain why each one is called a social factor.
2. How do (i) the media, and (ii) values and behaviour, affect health and wellbeing?
3. What is the difference between wealth and income?
4. Why doesn't winning the lottery and becoming a millionaire make a person upper class?
5. Identify six health choices and explain why they are referred to in this way.
6. How do social factors affect our health choices? Choose one factor to explain this.
7. How do social factors affect whether we seek medical care?
8. How do social factors affect our levels of stress and anxiety? Choose one factor to explain this.

Assessment activity 4.3   2C.P4 | 2C.M3 | 2C.D3

As a youth worker at a youth centre in a big town, you have already produced a series of leaflets for the local healthcare centre to help raise awareness of the effects of primary and secondary socialisation on the health and wellbeing of young people, and of the influence of different types of relationships and the potential positive and negative ways these can influence their health and wellbeing.

The staff at the centre ask you to extend your leaflets to produce a report to show parents and their children the effect of a variety of different social factors and their link to overall health and wellbeing, with relevant examples.

Tips

When describing how social factors can affect the health and wellbeing of individuals, you should include the effects of at least four social factors, such as income, education, family and the media, on the person's health and wellbeing. Explain the wider effects of these social factors on the overall health and wellbeing of individuals, supporting this with detailed examples of the effects of each social factor. Evaluate the link between social factors, and consider the impact on the health and wellbeing of individuals in terms of physical, intellectual, emotional and social wellbeing.

How can we improve the health and wellbeing of the nation? Why do we need to try to do this and what are the benefits? Health and social care professionals can help people make healthy lifestyle choices and understand how to reduce risks to their health. This in turn can help prevent many diseases, illnesses and injuries.

Health promotion is the area of healthcare that raises awareness of these issues and educates us on how to follow healthier lifestyles. It helps us take more control over our own health and hopefully improve it. Health promotion is an important part of a number of roles in the health and social care sector, including health visitors, midwives, school nurses and GP practice nurses.

In this unit you will look at some of the reasons health promotion activities are carried out and the benefits of this work to both individuals and the general health and wellbeing of the nation. You will also explore the different forms of health promotion activities that are used by health and social care workers. Finally you will be given the opportunity to explore and research an area of health risk and then create materials for a health promotion activity for a specific target group. This will give you a valuable insight into this important aspect of health and social care work.

Assessment: You will be assessed by a series of assignments set by your teacher/tutor.

Learning aims

In this unit you will:

A explore the purpose, types and benefits of health promotion

B investigate how health risks can be addressed through health promotion.

> I found from listening to a GP practice nurse talk about her job that some people are not happy to be told how to live a more healthy lifestyle. However, by talking to them and explaining the benefits of making healthier choices, you can aid people's understanding. They are then more likely to take control of their situation and make their own decisions in choosing healthier lifestyle options.
>
> Hollie, *16-year-old would-be nurse*

Promoting Health and Wellbeing

BTEC
Assessment Zone

This table shows you what you must do in order to achieve a **Pass**, **Merit** or **Distinction** grade, and where you can find activities in this book to help you.

Assessment criteria

Level 1	Level 2 Pass	Level 2 Merit	Level 2 Distinction
Learning aim A: Explore the purpose, types and benefits of health promotion			
1A.1 State what is meant by health promotion, identifying the purpose and aim(s) of one health-promotion activity.	**2A.P1** Describe health promotion and the purpose and aims of three different health-promotion activities. **Assessment activity 5.1 See page 115.**		
1A.2 Outline how health promotion is used to benefit individuals.	**2A.P2** Describe how different types of health promotion are used to benefit the health and wellbeing of individuals and the nation. **Assessment activity 5.1 See page 115.**	**2A.M1** Maths Discuss how different types of health promotion are used to benefit the health and wellbeing of individuals and the nation, using selected examples. **Assessment activity 5.1 See page 115.**	**2A.D1** Maths Analyse the benefits of different types of health promotion to individuals and the nation, using selected examples. **Assessment activity 5.1 See page 115.**
Learning aim B: Investigate how health risks can be addressed through health promotion			
1B.3 Identify the main effects of the chosen health risk on individuals.	**2B.P3** English Describe the chosen health risk and its main effects on individuals, using research findings from different sources. **Assessment activity 5.2 See page 125.**	**2B.M2** English Explain how the chosen health risk affects individuals and how these effects can be addressed through health promotion, using research findings from different types of sources. **Assessment activity 5.2 See page 125.**	**2B.D2** English Evaluate the strategies used to address the chosen health risk, using research findings. **Assessment activity 5.2 See page 125.**
1B.4 English Maths Produce materials for a health-promotion activity, with guidance.	**2B.P4** English Maths Produce appropriate materials for a health-promotion activity, describing the health risk and health advice. **Assessment activity 5.2 See page 125.**	**2B.M3** English Maths Produce materials for a health-promotion activity tailored to a target group, describing the health risk and health advice. **Assessment activity 5.2 See page 125.**	**2B.D3** English Maths Make recommendations for how the health-promotion materials could be adapted for a different target group. **Assessment activity 5.2 See page 125.**

 English English signposting

 Maths Mathematics signposting

How you will be assessed

The unit will be assessed by a series of internally assessed tasks. You will be expected to show an understanding of health-promotion activities in the health and social care sectors. The tasks will be based on a scenario where you work in a local health or social care organisation. For example, the local youth service has become concerned about the health of young people in the area. They have approached your health and social care department to see whether there should be a local health promotion campaign.

Your assessment could be in the form of:

- an article or report on health risks faced by teenagers, which must include:
    - a description of health promotion and its purpose and aims, using three different examples
    - an explanation of a chosen health risk and how it affects teenagers
    - an explanation of how these effects could be addressed through health promotion
    - an evaluation of the benefits of health promotion to both teenagers and the nation

- an accompanying PowerPoint presentation, with slides and presentation notes

- a health-promotion campaign presented as an information pack containing posters, leaflets, booklets and a wall display, which could be given out locally and could be adapted for a different target group.

What is health promotion?

Introduction

Health promotion activities are an important part of a number of roles in the health and social care sector. In this topic you will learn what health promotion is and about its purpose and aims.

What is it?

Health promotion is the provision of information and education both to individuals and to the **nation,** which will enable them to make positive lifestyle choices. It enables people to take control over factors that affect their own health and so do something to improve their health and wellbeing. Health promotion cannot be imposed on people; it is done so that people are given sufficient good and accurate information for them to make up their own minds on actions to take that will make a positive change.

What is its purpose?

The purpose of health promotion is to inform people about current thinking on how to live healthily. It aims to motivate people to adopt healthy lifestyle choices. Health promotion should be **proactive** in tackling health-related challenges and issues. An example of an issue that can be targeted by health promotion is the rising incidence of obesity in this country and the problems that arise from this, such as cost to the NHS of treatment for conditions arising from obesity and the increase in obesity-related deaths.

What are the aims of health promotion?

Health promotion activities aim to:

- raise health awareness. An example might be a campaign to raise awareness of the dangers of high blood pressure and how to keep blood pressure down.
- encourage safety and reduce accidents. For example, a television campaign might show a child being hit by a car travelling at 30 mph, to demonstrate that even speeds considered quite slow still maim or kill. The aim of this would be to encourage people to drive more slowly and so reduce the incidence and severity of such accidents.
- reduce the number of people smoking. Health-promotion activities raise awareness of the dangers of smoking, explain how people can access help to stop smoking and provide strategies to help them give up.
- encourage healthy eating habits. Providing information about the hows and whys of healthy eating helps people make better food choices. This can have the effect of reducing the incidence of obesity or undernourishment in the population, and their effects, such as poor health, poorer quality of life and shorter life expectancy.

• reduce alcohol intake. Information on the risks of excess alcohol consumption and guidance on safe weekly levels may encourage people to cut down their alcohol intake, improving their own health and life expectancy, and reducing alcohol-induced antisocial behaviour.

Activity — Health promotion campaigns

1 Look at the material in the illustration. Do you recognise this health promotion campaign on strokes? If not, look at the website by visiting Pearson hotlinks. You can access this by going to www.pearsonhotlinks.co.uk and searching for this title. This campaign was launched by the Public Health Agency (PHA) in June 2011.

2 Make a list of the different types of health-promotion activities that form part of the campaign.

3 Download a FAST leaflet and read it.

4 Identify how the campaign meets each of the purposes and aims mentioned in this topic. To do this draw up a table with the purpose and the five aims in the left-hand column. Include two more columns for you to say how the campaign meets the purpose or aim, and what is good about the campaign. You may think that a campaign about strokes has nothing to do with healthy eating, smoking or alcohol, but it does. You will need to do some research into the possible causes of strokes to understand why.

5 What are the possible consequences of someone suffering a stroke not getting help fast enough?

6 In a group of two or three, role-play a person suffering a stroke with someone else being with them or finding them quickly and following the steps shown in the health-promotion campaign. If you have three in your group, the third person can be a paramedic or an emergency department doctor. Be prepared to show your role play to the rest of the class.

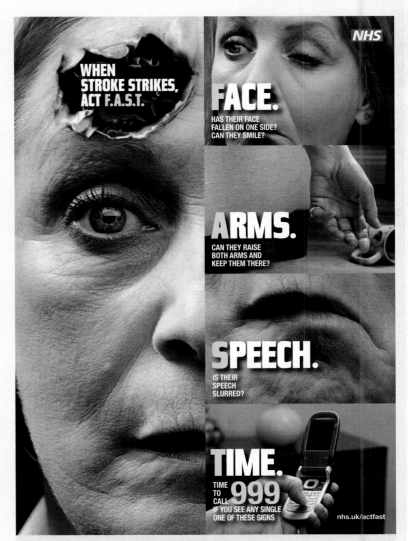

Do you recognise this health promotion campaign?

Types of health promotion

Key terms

Screening – mass checking of sectors of the population for early signs of a particular disease or condition.

Immunisation – to make someone immune to a disease, usually by vaccination.

Vaccination – the introduction of a very small quantity of a weakened form of a disease into the body, usually by injection, to help the body develop antibodies to that particular disease.

Introduction

Health promotion activities can take the forms of health-risk advice, health-promotion campaigns and medical intervention.

Health-risk advice raises awareness of health-related issues and educates individuals to help them to make healthy lifestyle choices.

Health-promotion campaigns are local or national initiatives targeted at large audiences with the aim of raising awareness of health-related issues. There are various types of campaign, such as Department of Health national campaigns and national and local NHS campaigns. They use different media, such as television, cinema, the internet, magazines and newspapers, and leaflets.

Medical intervention is initiated by central government (e.g. the Department of Health) and includes programmes of **screening**, **immunisations** and **vaccinations** that are used to proactively reduce or eliminate disease.

Health-risk advice

There are many types of health-risk advice including:

- Peer education: rather than advice coming from health professionals, community members are supported to promote health-enhancing change among themselves, encouraging each other in healthy behaviour.
- Shock tactics: for instance, showing pictures of the inside of a dead smoker's lungs or close-up pictures of genitalia affected by a sexually transmitted infection.
- Advice from health professionals: in schools health professionals may be invited to speak to groups of learners on topics, such as drinking, smoking and safe sex. Health professionals also give advice in health and social care settings, such as doctors' surgeries or hospitals. They may be called upon, for example, to advise someone who has asthma and smokes or someone who needs an operation, but is too obese for this to be a safe option so needs to lose weight first.
- Advice from police and fire service: school-based police officers or police community support officers give advice in both primary and secondary schools as well as to other community groups on topics such as alcohol or keeping safe at Hallowe'en. The fire service talk about being safe on Bonfire Night, or any areas to do with fire safety.

Have you ever received health-risk advice at school?

- Testimonies from people personally affected by issues: this is when a person speaks about a health issue that has affected them. It can be in the context of a large-scale campaign, such as part of a television initiative against drink driving, or on a smaller scale such as an individual talking to a school or other community group, perhaps about the dangers of drug taking.

Examples of advice

Health advice can be given in a wide variety of forms and it can cover many topics.

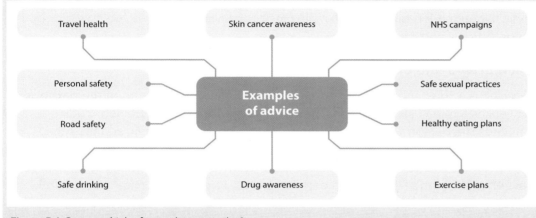

Figure 5.1 Can you think of any other examples?

One example of an area where health advice is needed in the UK is skin cancer awareness. The dangers of sun exposure in the development of skin cancer were not fully appreciated in Britain until relatively recently, with many people believing that in our temperate climate there was no need to protect ourselves from the sun. This is in stark contrast to Australia, where awareness is high because of the greater intensity of UV radiation from the sun there and the consequent very high incidence of skin cancer – four times higher than the UK, Canada and the USA.

There are many websites that help raise awareness of skin cancer. For example, the Cancer Research UK website explains that most skin cancers are caused by overexposure to ultraviolet radiation from the sun or sunbeds and recommends ways to enjoy the sun safely by staying in the shade, covering up and using at least SPF15 sunscreen for protection. There are video clips, information, photographs, an advice section and links to other useful websites, as well as details of their SunSmart campaign. The Skin Cancer Foundation website has similar information, including a Go With Your Own Glow campaign, which asks women to love and protect their skins, and videos aimed at teenagers showing the risks of sunbeds.

Activity   Skin cancer research

Do some research into the facts about skin cancer. Think about it. Do you, or any of your family or friends, ever go out in the sun without sunscreen? Do you ever use a sunbed? In a small group, discuss these questions and think about why people do these things.

Research the facts behind the causes of skin cancer to produce a poster that can be put up at school to persuade young people to:

- use sunscreen
- not use sunbeds.

Medical intervention and benefits

Introduction

In this topic you will learn about the different types and benefits of medical intervention.

Types of medical intervention

Medical intervention falls into two main categories: vaccination, including childhood immunisations, and screening.

Vaccinations and childhood immunisations

Key terms

Pathogen – a microorganism that causes disease, such as bacteria and viruses.

A vaccine is a substance that contains a weakened or synthetic form of the **pathogen** that causes a particular disease. It cannot cause the disease in a person, but it stimulates the person's immune system to recognise the pathogen, so that if the vaccinated person comes into contact with the disease again, their body will recognise it and produce the correct antibodies to destroy it. Vaccines are usually given by injection and include HPV (human papilloma virus, to prevent cervical cancer), influenza and pneumonia.

The process of building up immunity by taking a vaccine is called immunisation. Through immunisations, diseases such as tetanus and diphtheria have practically disappeared in the UK. Europe was declared polio free in 2002 thanks to immunisation. These diseases could come back, though, which is why it is important that children continue to be immunised. Practice or school nurses usually do this and each immunisation happens at a certain age, for example babies up to 15 months are immunised against polio, diphtheria, whooping cough and meningitis, and measles, mumps and rubella (MMR). Girls aged 12–13 are now immunised against HPV.

Activity   Immunisation

Draw up a table, and in the first column write the names of three of the vaccines mentioned. Do some research and in the second column write down the categories of people they are given to, including age group.

Screening

Women are invited for cervical screening from the age of 25.

Screening is a way of detecting cancer or other conditions at a very early stage, when they can best be treated. The NHS runs screening programmes for cervical, breast and bowel cancer and sight screening for people with diabetes.

The NHS Breast Screening Programme provides free breast screening every three years for all women aged 50 and over. Women are invited to have a mammogram. This is an X-ray of each breast taken while the breast is compressed. This can be uncomfortable, but it can detect small changes in breast tissue, which may indicate cancers that are too small to be felt either by the woman herself or by a doctor. In September 2000, research showed that the NHS Breast Screening Programme had lowered mortality rates from breast cancer in the 55–69 age group.

WorkSpace

◤ Elaine White

Mammogram Operator

I am a health professional working as a mammogram operator, as part of a small team in a mobile breast screening unit. A mammogram is an X-ray of the breast, taken to look for any abnormalities and so find breast cancer at an early stage when there is a good chance of successful treatment and full recovery. We are all women, even the receptionist who books clients in on arrival and tells them what to do, and the unit is parked in different parts of the area for a couple of weeks at a time, usually in a hospital car park. Local women are automatically sent an invitation for screening if they are 47 or above, every three years.

My main task is to produce an acceptable mammogram for every person who comes for screening. The breasts are X-rayed one at a time. I have to position the breast between the X-ray machine and a clear plate at the correct angle and firmly compress the breast between the plates so that it becomes thin enough for the radiation to pass through the breast tissue to produce a clear image. Many women are nervous about having their breasts handled by a stranger the first time they come so it is important that I put them at ease, reassuring them while treating it as an everyday experience, and showing compassion if anyone is really worried or even frightened. The process can be mildly uncomfortable for a very short period of time but does not usually hurt. I also have to be careful to record which mammogram belongs to which client so there is no confusion when results are sent out by post after the mammogram has been looked at carefully. About one in twenty women is called back for further assessment but only about one in six of those are diagnosed with breast cancer.

It is a very satisfying job, because screening saves about 1,400 lives a year, and it is good to know that by doing my job well I have contributed to that number. I do mammograms on women who have undergone gender reassignment so started life as a man, and have X-rayed breasts of every shape and size, so no one need feel embarrassed. I also get to meet women from every walk of life and they all react slightly differently to the experience so no two days are the same.

Think about it

1 Why are communication skills so important to Elaine's job?

2 What qualities does Elaine need to do her job successfully?

3 Explain why breast screening is an example of health promotion. What are its benefits?

4 Look at the diabetes screening programme. How is it different to breast cancer screening?

The benefits of health promotion to the health and wellbeing of an individual

Introduction

The World Health Organization has defined health promotion as 'the process of enabling people to increase control over, and to improve, their health'. In this topic you will look at the benefits of health promotion to the health and wellbeing of us all as individuals.

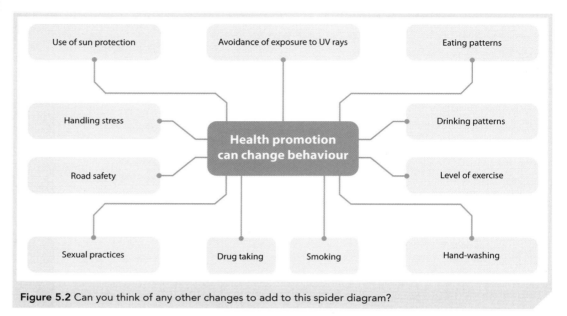

Figure 5.2 Can you think of any other changes to add to this spider diagram?

Benefits

Health promotion can do the following:

- Increase our understanding of health issues: for example, health promotion leaflets on the over-use of **antibiotics**, and the resulting consequences in the form of **superbugs**, have helped inform the public as to why the doctor won't prescribe antibiotics for a viral infection, such as a cold.

- Increase our responsibility for our own health: for example, understanding how to lift an object safely means a person is less likely to lift a heavy load wrongly (i.e. without bending the knees) and so help avoid back injury.

Activity   Safe working practices

1 There are many other examples of safe working practices that help us take responsibility for our own health, as well as examples of ways to take care of ourselves in other aspects of our lives. With a partner, write down as many ways as possible in which you can take responsibility for your own health.

2 Compare your list with those of other groups. Each group should then take one different point and prepare an information leaflet to promote it.

- Decrease risk of disease and/or injury: for example, health promotion about how the HIV virus can be transmitted has reduced the number of people developing AIDS.

- Improve quality of life: health promotion can raise awareness of ways to tackle a particular problem, e.g. giving obese people more strategies to help them lose weight and consequently improve their quality of life.

- Increase **life expectancy**: for instance, informing people of the levels of alcohol considered to be safe to consume in a week. By keeping to these limits people can increase their life expectancy.

- Change people's personal behaviour practices and lifestyle choices. For example, it is widely accepted that there is a correct technique to good hand washing, and separate studies from around the world show that good hand hygiene practices can reduce illness, sickness absence and the associated costs by up to 40 per cent. Hand washing is one of the most important ways of controlling the spread of infection, especially those that cause diarrhoea and vomiting, and respiratory disease.

However, although most of us think we wash our hands thoroughly and effectively it is not until we watch a demonstration on the correct way to wash hands that we realise that we don't do it as well as we think.

Another good example of the benefit to the individual of changing personal behaviour and lifestyle is smoking. It is better for people to improve their own health by giving up smoking rather than relying on health care professionals to try to help them once they have become ill with a smoking-related condition such as lung cancer or emphysema.

Activity   Washing your hands

1 Look on the internet at some of the information sheets on how to wash your hands properly. Decide as a class which you think are the best ones, print them off and have a go at doing it properly.

2 Think of a way of encouraging more learners in your school to wash their hands properly. Devise a health-promotion activity to do this, including facts as to how it will improve their personal health and wellbeing.

When should you wash your hands and use sanitizer?

The benefits of health promotion to the nation (1)

Introduction

This topic looks at how health promotion benefits the nation by reducing levels of illness and disease, taking pressure off the NHS and reducing costs; by reducing levels of crime and by increasing the uptake of vaccination and screening programmes.

Reducing levels of illness and disease

Reduction in the incidence of heart disease is an example of the positive effect of health promotion. A study by the British Heart Foundation Health Promotion Research Group at the University of Oxford in January 2012 reported that heart attack deaths dropped by more than half between 2002 and 2010, due in part to the prevention of heart attacks by better management of risk factors, such as smoking, high cholesterol levels and high blood pressure. Much of this improvement can be attributed to health promotion.

The study also showed that too many heart attack victims still died before medical help arrived, so the British Heart Foundation has made a video showing how to do hands-only **CPR**. This video has had high exposure on television and has a pop-up link on various websites. As well as the video there is a blog, T-shirts, a petition to get CPR taught in schools, an opportunity to download the music ('Stayin' Alive' by the Bee Gees) and a free mobile app. It is hoped that these measures will increase public awareness and knowledge so that more deaths can be prevented by early use of CPR.

Impact on crime levels

Health promotion has also been shown to reduce crime levels. The taking of recreational drugs has been tackled with programmes that help support people in living a drug-free life, such as the Home Office strategy promoted in 2010 aimed at reducing demand, restricting supply and building recovery for drug users. Other campaigns, including Talk to Frank, on both TV and the internet, have also had an impact. Getting addicts off drugs results in fewer drug-related crimes, such as people stealing to fund a drug habit. Similarly, there are national strategies and campaigns aimed at reducing alcohol consumption, and therefore alcohol-related violent crime, by raising awareness of the possible consequences of drunkenness, such as injury and death.

Key terms

CPR – cardiopulmonary resuscitation, a means to resuscitate someone whose breathing or heartbeat has ceased.

Cervix – the entrance to the uterus from the vagina.

Did you know?

There were 8,790 alcohol-related deaths in the UK in 2010, 126 more than in 2009.

1 Do some research to find three pieces of health promotion material that could have an impact on crime levels.

2 Produce a PowerPoint® presentation that includes these three pieces of health promotion. Pick the piece that is best in your opinion and find some recent statistics to back up how it could have contributed to reducing crime levels in the UK. For further information visit the Office for National Statistics website. You can access this by going to www.pearsonhotlinks.co.uk and searching for this title.

3 Show it to the rest of the class, explaining why you think this is the best piece and presenting your statistics.

Increased uptake in vaccination and screening programmes

By promoting the need for a certain vaccination nationally and, where possible, combining this with a screening programme, some diseases can be greatly reduced or even eradicated. One example is cervical cancer. Cancer Research UK reports that this is the second most common cancer in women under the age of 35, with 2,900 women a year in the UK diagnosed with the disease. The national Department of Health HPV (Human Papilloma Virus) vaccination programme was started in September 2008 for girls aged 12 and 13, to protect against the commonest cause of cervical cancer. It was also offered to older girls aged 14 to 17 over three years to make sure they didn't miss the protection. The 'cervical cancer jab' is delivered mainly through secondary schools. It is estimated that about 400 lives a year could be saved in the UK as a result of this programme.

The NHS Cervical Screening Programme was introduced in the 1980s. A cervical screening test, or smear test, is a way of detecting abnormal, pre-cancerous cells in the **cervix** of women aged between 25 and 64. By detecting and treating these cells about three-quarters of cancers can be prevented from developing. Since the programme's introduction the number of cervical cancer cases has decreased by about seven each year. Combined with the HPV vaccination, cervical screening continues to be an important step towards preventing cervical cancer.

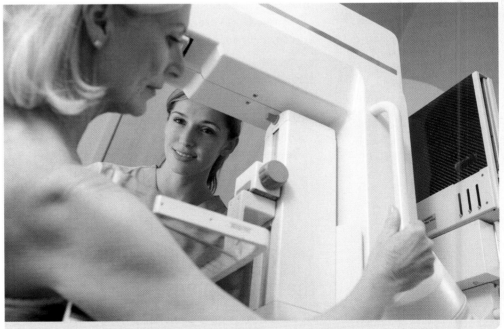

What other screening programmes can you think of?

The benefits of health promotion to the nation (2)

Introduction

Other benefits to the nation of health promotion include addressing high-profile health and wellbeing concerns and reducing financial cost to the NHS.

Addressing high-profile health and wellbeing concerns

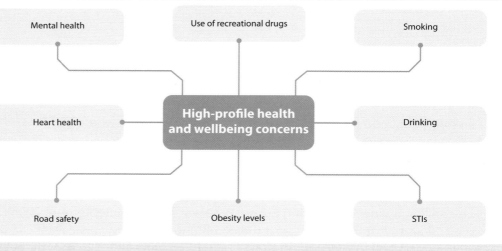

Figure 5.3 Are there any other issues you would expect to be on this diagram?

Obesity, especially in children, is a current high-profile concern. At the time of writing, the latest Health Survey for England (HSE) showed that nearly one in four adults (a quarter) and over one in ten children aged between two and ten (a tenth) are **obese.** Obesity can severely affect a person's health, increasing the risk of some cancers, heart and liver diseases, and type 2 diabetes.

Key terms

Obese – having a **body mass index (BMI)** of 30 or more.

Body Mass Index (BMI) – a method of determining the proportion of body fat a person has, found by dividing a person's weight measured in kg by the square of their height in metres.

Activity   Health promotion work

Do some research on the internet into the health-promotion work being done by either Change4Life or Cancer Research UK. Produce a PowerPoint presentation to show what you have learned.

Reduced financial cost to the NHS and the government

Heath promotion also aims to help reduce financial costs. For example, the direct cost of treating obesity, plus the costs involved in treating conditions for which obesity is a likely contributory factor, are estimated to be £4.2 billion a year and are forecast to more than double by 2050 if we carry on as we are. As well as the conditions already mentioned, other health risks include stroke and osteoarthritis. There are additional costs for equipment, operations and other related services.

Other areas where health promotion aims to reduce costs are smoking and alcohol consumption. The British Heart Foundation research in 2005 showed that treating disease directly caused by smoking, such as lung cancer and emphysema, costs more than £5 billion a year in the UK. This figure is likely to be an underestimate, because it does not include indirect costs, such as lost productivity and informal care, the costs of treating disease caused by passive smoking, and other conditions associated with smoking. It also showed that smoking costs five times more than lack of physical activity, twice as much as obesity and about the same as an unhealthy diet.

Activity   Reducing health costs

1 These facts show how much obesity, smoking and alcohol are costing the NHS and the government. In pairs, research the most recent health-promotion campaigns on smoking and alcohol. One example is the hard-hitting television campaign showing children appealing to their parents not to smoke. Try to find videos of these campaigns and if there are any leaflets or posters produced as part of the same campaign. Put together a package to sum up each campaign you find, so you can report back to the rest of the class.

2 Another area where cost can be reduced by health promotion is the police and prison services. Do some more research to see how health promotion affects these two services. Find some current data showing trends to report back to the class.

Assessment activity 5.1   *Maths*   2A.P1 | 2A.P2 | 2A.M1 | 2A.D1

You are a trainee nurse at a health centre in a big town. The local high school has become concerned about the health and lifestyles of some of the young people in the area and has approached your health centre to suggest that there should be a local health-promotion campaign. You have been asked to produce a report on health risks faced by teenagers. This must include the following:

- An introduction describing what is meant by health promotion with details of three different health risks that may affect teenagers and one health promotion activity that has already been carried out related to each health risk, describing the purpose and aim of each activity.

- An explanation of a chosen health risk relevant to teenagers in your area and at your school/college, such as obesity, drug taking or alcohol, and how it affects teenagers.

- How these effects could be addressed through health promotion.

- An evaluation of the strategies already being used in your area and nationally to address the chosen health risk.

- An analysis of the benefits of health promotion both to teenagers and to the nation, using selected examples.

You need to produce a PowerPoint presentation with notes on handouts to sum up your findings and conclusions to accompany your report.

Tips

You must use evidence to support your arguments, such as information from media articles and summaries of health reports, and should refer to the wider benefits of health promotion such as economic and social benefits.

When you analyse the benefits of health promotion, consider both the various benefits of health promotion and the links between benefits to individuals and the nation. You should refer either to a couple of examples in detail, such as one instance of health-risk advice and one instance of medical intervention, or to a wider range of illustrative examples if you decide to look at a range of health-promotion activities.

Targeting selected health risks

Getting started ▶▶

What health risks do you think the teenagers in your school/college are most likely to be affected by in the immediate future? What evidence have you got for this? Discuss this with a partner and see if they agree.

Introduction

This topic suggests some possible health risks to young people. We will also look at some possible sources of information for your research.

◤ Topics for health promotion

Some of the health topics currently being promoted are:

- substance misuse, e.g. recreational drugs, solvents
- binge drinking
- safe sex
- healthy eating
- smoking
- road safety
- hand washing
- participation in sport and exercise.

For your assignment for this part of the unit you need to pick a health risk and research its associated effects on health. You will need to gather information such as is shown in Figure 5.4, for smoking.

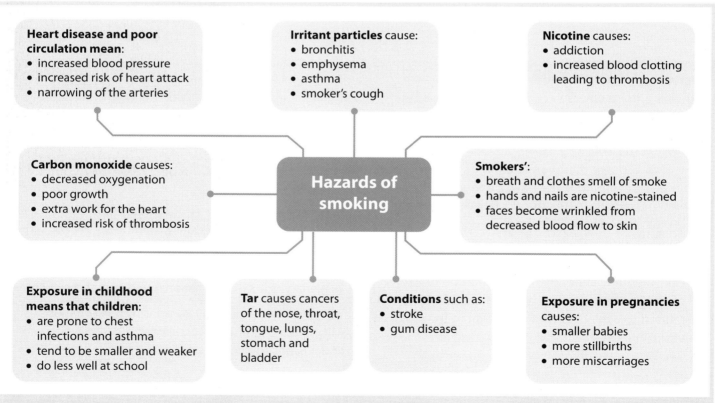

Heart disease and poor circulation mean:
- increased blood pressure
- increased risk of heart attack
- narrowing of the arteries

Irritant particles cause:
- bronchitis
- emphysema
- asthma
- smoker's cough

Nicotine causes:
- addiction
- increased blood clotting leading to thrombosis

Carbon monoxide causes:
- decreased oxygenation
- poor growth
- extra work for the heart
- increased risk of thrombosis

Hazards of smoking

Smokers':
- breath and clothes smell of smoke
- hands and nails are nicotine-stained
- faces become wrinkled from decreased blood flow to skin

Exposure in childhood means that children:
- are prone to chest infections and asthma
- tend to be smaller and weaker
- do less well at school

Tar causes cancers of the nose, throat, tongue, lungs, stomach and bladder

Conditions such as:
- stroke
- gum disease

Exposure in pregnancies causes:
- smaller babies
- more stillbirths
- more miscarriages

Figure 5.4 Can you think of any more physical hazards of smoking?

You will also need to work out the intellectual, emotional and social impacts of these possible physical effects to be able to fully understand the total effect of smoking on an individual's health.

Researching health risks

Choose the health risk you think you might want as the focus of your assignment. Do some research on its effects on an individual's health and divide the information up into effects on an individual's physical, intellectual, emotional and social (PIES) needs. You could do this as a mind map or in a table.

Forms of health-promotion materials

Health-promotion materials include posters, leaflets, games, presentations, web-based materials, CDs, DVDs, flyers, newspaper adverts or articles, TV and radio coverage and wall displays. They may accompany campaigns launched on the TV or internet. All should be easy to understand, attractive and accurate.

- Posters: should be eye-catching and not contain a lot of writing. They should give either telephone numbers or website addresses where help can be sought or more information can be found.

- Leaflets: contain more information than a poster, but should still be attractive, easy to understand, accurate and contain the information needed by the target group or groups, such as useful telephone numbers or websites.

- Games: examples include board games to persuade young children to clean their teeth and card games which teach facts about alcohol to teenagers in a fun way.

- Presentations: a popular form is PowerPoint and these can be very effective if each slide is kept simple, with a few bullet points and a diagram on each, so the person doing the presentation talks about each slide rather than reading them out. Special effects and diagrams can be incorporated and diagrams can be imported to make it attractive, hard-hitting and entertaining.

- Wall displays: the NHS website leaflet, *Effective Displays: A Guide*, suggests that the six rules for an effective display are (i) deliver the message, (ii) consider the display location, (iii) link to current campaigns, (iv) use a variety of materials to enhance your display, (v) make it readable, and (vi) arrange the display to give impact.

SWINE FLU INFORMATION
0800 1 513 513
www.nhs.uk
www.direct.gov.uk/swineflu

IMPORTANT INFORMATION ABOUT SWINE FLU

This leaflet contains important information to help you and your family – **KEEP IT SAFE**

Did this poster catch your eye? Why?

Wall display

Download the guide from the NHS website if possible and produce your own wall display, based on the health risk you have been focusing on, following the six rules. You can do this in a small group with others who are working on the same risk. All groups should then judge the displays to see if they have stuck to the rules. Were any of them out of your control?

Promotional materials

Draw up a table showing each type of health promotion material mentioned, and any others you can think of, in the first column. Then add columns headed 'strengths' and 'weaknesses' for each type, and complete the table.

Research and data gathering (1)

Introduction

There are many different sources to use for research. Primary sources are first-hand sources of information where, for example, you speak to a school nurse about her work. You are gathering information that doesn't already exist. Secondary sources are those giving information which is second-hand, using sources such as books and the internet.

Research using different sources

Only use information that you understand yourself and put it in your own words.

Some examples of sources of information are:

- Websites: Remember that unlike books and journals, information on the net hasn't necessarily being checked. Search engines such as Google put the websites that are used most often at the top, so providing you search for the health risk in the UK by clicking on the 'Pages from the UK' option, check the date on the information and work from the top of the list of websites shown by a search engine, you should have current and useful information. Quote the website address in your bibliography.

- Books: always check the date a book has been published, as information in a book that is several years old may now be outdated. You can do this by looking on the copyright page. Use the contents or index to find the section you need. When quoting a book in a bibliography at the end of your work the correct way is to write the author (surname followed by initial/s), the year of publication, the title of the book and the publisher.

- Newspapers/magazines: these can be useful sources of information, but much of the content of these sorts of publication are the opinions of the author of the article, unless they are quoting from a specific piece of research. Be careful to distinguish between facts and opinions and quote not only the name of the newspaper/magazine and its date of publication,

What are the advantages and disadvantages of using books instead of websites?

but also the title and author of the article or feature if known.

- Leaflets: these can be picked up from a wide range of places, such as libraries, health centres, hospitals and even supermarkets. Again, make sure they are up-to-date, quote the title and the body publishing the leaflet and any other information available, such as a date. Some leaflets show more of this sort of information than others.

- Journals: many professional bodies produce their own journals, such as the *Nursing Times* for nursery nurses. Quote sources of articles in the same way as those in newspapers/magazines.

- DVDs and TV programmes: these are useful as they often show real-life situations, can be watched by lots of people at once and are easy to use and engage with. When quoting information from them make sure you show you know what is fact and what is opinion or fiction, and that it is up-to-date.

Other research sources

- Department of Health: this government department is in charge of public health, adult social care and the NHS. It is headed by the Secretary of State for Health (who is a Cabinet minister), supported by health ministers (who are MPs), and professional officers (who are leaders in their professions and provide the department with expert knowledge about health and social care issues). The department produces a wide array of publications and has a very useful website. You can access this by going to www.pearsonhotlinks.co.uk and searching for this title.

- Health professionals: you can gather information from health professionals by interviewing them, giving them a **questionnaire** to complete or listening to them talk either in your school or in their place of work and making notes. You need to think carefully beforehand about what exactly you want to find out and have your questions ready, but also be prepared to ask supplementary questions depending on how the conversation goes. Don't ask questions that are too personal as these will make the person feel awkward or uncomfortable.

- Service users: again, you can conduct a **survey** with service users by giving the person a questionnaire. Be careful not to put too much reliance on one person's answers, because they may be biased.

Remember

Use the communication skills you learned in Unit 3.

Key terms

Questionnaire – a list of questions in writing, designed to gather information on a specific subject.

Survey – a broad investigation of a subject, often informed by asking questions of a representative group.

Activity   Surveying school/college life

As a group, conduct a **survey** of an aspect of school or college life, such as the safety of the site or what learners prefer to eat at lunchtime. Discuss in your group what went well and what went less well. Write a report based on your findings and include an evaluation of how effective your techniques were for gathering the information you needed.

Research and data gathering (2)

Gathering data

Data is information, often in number form or statistics. It is important that you collect data on the health topic you select as the focus for your assignment. Before you start collecting data you have to be clear about what your aim is and what methods you are going to use so you don't end up collecting irrelevant data. When you have gathered the data you must decide how to present it, for instance in a report or in some form of diagram.

Examples of types of data include:

- National **statistics**: these are collected from a wide sample of the population of the UK by many national organisations, for example the UK Statistics Authority. One of the areas it covers is health and social care. The Office for National Statistics, the government statistics service, also has its own website. However, although you will come across these websites through search engines, the content is quite hard to understand, so you might prefer to use the Department of Health's website, as this has information that is more readily understandable.

- Local statistics: these are collected by many agencies, including local government. It is their responsibility to collect local data and submit it to the government when asked to. They provide information, advice and support for all local residents, so their websites provide a valuable source of data. You can also collect statistics from your community, such as your school or college, but be sure to ask a large enough sample of people to make your conclusions meaningful.

- Case studies: these are detailed descriptions of a person's life or work. Two useful sources are the CareUK and Macmillan Nurses websites. These provide a useful insight into how health issues affect individuals.

Think about interesting and clear ways to present your data.

Activity   Local statistics

1 Go to your local council's website. Look to see what information they have on health issues in your area, in particular the one you are thinking of basing your assignment on.

2 Produce a PowerPoint presentation with no more than six slides to show to the class about a local health issue. It must include some data in diagram form.

WorkSpace

April Forrester

School Nurse

I am a school nurse based in a small town. I work in a team that includes three early years workers, other health professionals and various support staff. We have a base, but I spend most of my time in the various secondary schools to which I am allocated.

My main task is to provide preventative health services to help the learners grow and develop in the best way possible. I identify problems and provide services, such as health education, and referral to other services and care, in order to prevent more serious problems developing later, which would be more difficult to deal with and more costly to address. I work with groups of, and individual, learners. I sometimes speak to a whole year group about an issue, and hold drop-in clinics at schools for any learners to come along and have a private chat with me. Issues they talk to me about are very varied, from unwanted pregnancies to personal hygiene or problems with parents and friends. I have a full range of printed health-promotion materials available, so I can give learners leaflets, which tell them where to find more help if needed. I can also refer them to more specialist agencies that can help them with their specific problems.

I help at school events, such as learning days, when a health input is required, and work with other nurses to carry out year group vaccinations, such as HPV. It is a very satisfying job, because although I speak to many learners when they are upset or worried, it is good to feel that I am helping them, and as no two problems are exactly the same it is a very varied job, so never boring. Sometimes it is very sad, such as when a relative, friend, learner or teacher has died, and learners need to talk through their feelings, but it is often fun, as I really enjoy working with young people.

Think about it

1 Why are communication skills so important to April's job?
2 How does April promote health among young people?
3 How can you make use of health-promotion materials to make sure you keep yourself fit and healthy?

Target groups in health promotion

Introduction

The target group of health-promotion materials can be almost anyone: children, adolescents, employees, men, women, the old, the young and so on. But what is important to note is that campaigns are much more effective if they are targeted at a specific group and tailored to meet that group's needs. General campaigns have been proven to be far less effective as people tend to feel the message is not aimed specifically at them.

Target-group appropriate health-promotion materials

There are many ways in which health-promotion materials can be made appropriate to a target group. They include:

- Language: plain language, without the use of jargon or technical terms, is very important in communicating health information to everyone. The level of readability of materials should be appropriate to the age and ability of the target group. It is important, for instance, that materials aimed at children have few words and are simple and straightforward. Materials should also be available in the range of languages that reflects the make-up of the target group.

- Images: images used for children should be appealing and make them feel safe, whereas those aimed at teenagers and older groups can be more hard-hitting and thought-provoking. Images can include photographs, movies, cartoons, symbols and artworks.

- Activity: some health-promotion materials ask that groups of people take part in a specific activity. The physical requirement of the activity should be appropriate to the target group. It would be inappropriate, for instance, to ask a group of people with limited mobility to do an exercise that involved doing star jumps.

- Position of display: think about your target group. If you have a display high on a wall, you will immediately rule out people below a certain height and wheelchair users. Similarly, if you have the display in a poorly lit corner, those with a visual impairment may not be able to read the display. Also think about the general environment where you place your display: there is little point, for instance, in putting something about childcare in an residential care home for older people.

- Timing: the timing of the use of health-promotion materials can be crucial; for instance, material about the safe use of fireworks and bonfires should be launched a few weeks before Bonfire Night and Diwali, and drink-drive campaigns are effective during the period of Christmas and New Year, when more people fall victim to this than at other times of the year because of all the extra parties.

Ethics

The consideration of **ethics** is very important when planning health promotion. The different aspects you need to think about are:

- Is the health promotion necessary?
- What can you do with regard to your health-promotion campaign that will place the smallest limit on people's **civil liberties**?
- Will it be effective?
- Is it proportionate? For example, the drink-driving laws are a serious curb on the freedom of individuals to drink what they want when they drive. However, the potential harm that drink-drivers could do to themselves and others makes the current laws fair and proportionate.
- Is there a public justification? A health promotion should affect the nation as a whole, not just the individual who changes their behaviour as a result of it.

Activity — Ethical considerations in health promotion

In a group, take a recent example of a health promotion. Compare the health promotion to the list of ethical considerations above and come up with a list of reasons for and against each point. Present your arguments on both sides back to the class and allow them to vote on whether the health promotion was ethical or not.

Forms of media

The success of health promotion can often depend on the media used to do the promotion. For instance, women over 50 tend to read particular types of magazine and so using a young person's magazine to promote the Nation Breast Screening Programme would not work. Similarly, when targeting adolescents about an issue such as safe sex, it is better to use posters in places such as schools, colleges and youth centres, internet pop-ups, and adverts shown at the cinema before films aimed at teenagers.

Have you been influenced by adverts shown on social networking sites?

How materials could be adapted for different target groups

Introduction

The planning and producing of a national health-promotion campaign is very expensive. It is therefore more cost-effective if materials can be produced and then adapted for different target groups.

In adapting materials you would need to look at the following:

- Changing the language: making translated materials available to meet the unique cultural needs of a local population. Translation software or specialist agencies can translate documents and materials downloaded from websites, such as the Department of Health's.

- Changing the style of language: a campaign could use text message style spelling or street language to communicate with teenagers, whereas a more formal style of language would be used with older people.

- Using Braille: materials can be printed in Braille so that blind people can access leaflets and posters.

- Easier language: this is necessary so that people with learning difficulties can understand what they are reading or hearing. If you are adapting a message for children, it might also be necessary to simplify the language.

- Larger print: this enables people with sight impairments to access the information.

- Using a different media form: materials can be made into audio CDs for those who have sight impairment or made into videos for those with hearing impairments or learning difficulties or who don't read very well. The images can be changed to appeal to different groups.

One example is the NHS's free *NHS Stop Smoking Start Living* booklet, which is available as an audio CD, in Braille, in large print, and in an easy-to-read version for people with learning difficulties, as well as in 9 languages other than English. The website and the TV campaign, launched at the start of 2012, advertise a free Quit Kit – a box of practical tools and advice developed with experts, smokers and ex-smokers, which has helped thousands of smokers quit successfully – to use alongside the booklet.

Pages from the Easy-read Go Smokefree Guide for people with learning difficulties.

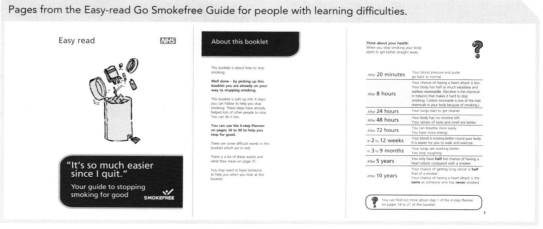

Source: smokefree.nhs.uk © Department of Health.

Evaluation

It is important that all health-promotion materials are **evaluated** to make sure they are appropriate to the target group, and that the strategy used in producing and launching them is effective. Existing campaigns are evaluated and lessons learned from how successful, or not, they have been.

Assessment

Here are some questions to test what you have learned so far and a practice assessment assignment for you to try.

Key terms

Evaluate – gather and review evidence, and make a judgement as to success.

Just checking

1 Name three possible topics for health promotion.
2 Pick one of the topics you named in question 1, which is not the one you are basing your assignment on, and describe its effects on an individual's health and wellbeing.
3 Name three possible primary sources of evidence.
4 Name two possible secondary sources of evidence.
5 Name a source of national statistics.
6 Which body could provide you with local health statistics?
7 Explain why 'type of service user' is a target group? Give an example.
8 Name three factors in making health promotion materials appropriate to a target group.
9 How can health promotion materials be adapted for different target groups? Include at least three ways in your answer.
10 Why do groups producing health promotion materials evaluate the success of existing campaigns?

Assessment activity 5.2   *English   Maths*   2B.P3 | 2B.P4 | 2B.M2 | 2B.M3 | 2B.D2 | 2B.D3

You are a trainee nurse at a health centre in a big town. Following your successful report on health risks faced by teenagers it has been decided that it is necessary to run a health-promotion campaign.

You now need to pick a health risk and produce some materials that could be included in a pack that will be given out as part of this campaign in places such as youth and medical centres and libraries. The pack needs to contain posters, leaflets, booklets and material for a wall display that describe the health risk and give advice to teenagers.

You need to research and collect existing information on the health risk on which to base your materials. You will need to produce a short report on how the health risk can be addressed by health promotion and compare how successful different strategies have been in the past.

When you have produced your information pack, you will be expected to present the information to your peers, and recommend how the health promotion materials could be adapted for a different target group of your choice.

Tips

Don't forget to think about the effect of the health risk on physical, intellectual, emotional and social health.

Use research findings from at least two different sources.

Introduction

How often do you think about why you need to eat and what you are eating? Do you know how your body and health are affected by the food you eat? Although we know that some foods are not good for us, we might think that we have plenty of time to eat sensibly when we are older, but by then we might have developed a condition such as diabetes or coronary heart disease.

Health and social care workers must have a good understanding of the principles of nutrition so that they can maintain or improve their own health and that of service users or patients. You will learn what a balanced diet is and how an unbalanced diet can affect people's health. You will think about how dietary needs change over the lifespan, and conditions that require people to follow specific dietary plans or advice. You will explore the dietary needs of people of different religions, and other factors that influence what people choose to eat.

Assessment: You will be assessed by a series of assignments set by your teacher/tutor.

Learning aims

In this unit you will:

A explore the effects of balanced and unbalanced diets on the health and wellbeing of individuals

B understand the specific nutritional needs and preferences of individuals.

> I'm so glad I have learned something about nutrition. My dad had a heart attack last year, and the doctor told my mum it was because he was overweight and unfit. The whole family now thinks much more about what we eat and we are following a much healthier diet. We all take more exercise too. Doing it as a family has really helped Dad get better.
>
> Jamie, *17-year-old Health and Social Care learner*

The Impact of Nutrition on Health and Wellbeing

6

Assessment Zone

This table shows you what you must do in order to achieve a **Pass**, **Merit** or **Distinction** grade, and where you can find activities in this book to help you.

Assessment criteria			
Level 1	**Level 2 Pass**	**Level 2 Merit**	**Level 2 Distinction**
Learning aim A: Explore the effects of balanced and unbalanced diets on the health and wellbeing of individuals			
1A.1 Identify components of a balanced diet, giving examples of each.	**2A.P1** Describe the components of a balanced diet and their functions, sources and effects. **Assessment activity 6.1** **See page 141.**	**2A.M1** Compare the effects of balanced and unbalanced diets on the health and wellbeing of two individuals. **Assessment activity 6.1** **See page 141.**	**2A.D1** Assess the long-term effects of a balanced and unbalanced diet on the health and wellbeing of individuals. **Assessment activity 6.1** **See page 141.**
1A.2 Identify three effects of an unbalanced diet on the health and wellbeing of individuals.	**2A.P2** Describe the effects of an unbalanced diet on the health and wellbeing of individuals, giving examples of their causes. **Assessment activity 6.1** **See page 141.**		
Learning aim B: Understand the specific nutritional needs and preferences of individuals			
1B.3 Identify the specific dietary needs of an individual.	**2B.P3** Describe the specific dietary needs of two individuals at different life stages. **Assessment activity 6.2** **See page 154.**	**2B.M2** Explain the factors influencing the dietary choices of two individuals with specific dietary needs at different life stages. **Assessment activity 6.2** **See page 154.**	**2B.D2** Discuss how factors influence the dietary choices of two individuals with specific dietary needs at different life stages. **Assessment activity 6.2** **See page 154.**
1B.4 English Create, with guidance, a nutritional plan for a selected individual.	**2B.P4** English Create a nutritional plan for two individuals, with different specific nutritional needs. **Assessment activity 6.2** **See page 154.**	**2B.M3** Compare nutritional plans for two individuals with different nutritional needs. **Assessment activity 6.2** **See page 154.**	

English   English signposting

How you will be assessed

The unit will be assessed by a series of internally assessed tasks. You will be expected to show an understanding of nutrition across the lifespan. For example, the dietician at your health centre has planned a healthy eating week and has asked you to produce information for people that will provide a brief introduction to the components of a balanced diet, the effects on the body of an unbalanced diet, nutritional needs across the lifespan and specific dietary needs. You will also create a nutritional plan for two individuals.

Your assessment could be in the form of:

- a booklet
- a PowerPoint presentation to be shown on the TV screen in the waiting room
- case studies about individuals with specific dietary needs.

Components of a balanced diet (1)

▶ Essential nutrients

A balanced diet is made up of carbohydrates, proteins, fats, vitamins, minerals, fibre and water. Carbohydrates, proteins and fats are known as macronutrients because they are required in the body in large amounts.

Carbohydrates

Carbohydrates provide the main source of energy in the diet. These are sugars, starches and fibre. They include grains, pulses, fruit and vegetables, and should make up about 50 to 60 per cent of the diet.

Glucose is a simple sugar which is found in fruit, plants and the blood of animals. Glucose syrups are used in the manufacture of cakes, sweets and jams. These are digested more quickly than starches, so they can be absorbed and used more easily, but they cause peaks and troughs in blood glucose levels, so energy levels are much less stable. Table sugar is sucrose, a combination of two simple sugars, glucose and fructose.

Starches are found in wholemeal cereals, such as oats, wheat, barley, rye and rice. This group also includes potatoes, root vegetables, some fruits, and pulses and beans, such as lentils, baked beans and chickpeas. Some starches are refined and are present in foods such as pizza, which are often high in fat so should be limited in the diet.

When carbohydrates are eaten and digested, they break down into glucose, which is what we need to provide energy for the body. The glucose is absorbed into the bloodstream and a hormone called insulin is released by the pancreas to control the absorption of glucose into the cells.

Polysaccharides or fibre cannot be digested by the body but play an important role in adding bulk to faeces and helping to prevent constipation. A daily intake of 25g of fibre is recommended.

What carbohydrates can you identify in this photo?

Proteins

Protein is needed in the body for growth and repair. Proteins are made up of chains of amino acids and nine of them are essential. This means that you must obtain them from the food you eat because they can't be made in the body.

Proteins can be divided into animal and vegetable sources. Animal proteins include meat, fish, cheese and eggs, and contain all of the essential amino acids. Studies show that eating lots of red and processed meat can contribute to stomach and bowel cancer. Plant proteins include pulses such as nuts, beans, peas and soya or tofu. They are high in fibre, vitamins and minerals, and low in fat. They contribute to disease prevention and good health, but do not contain all of the essential amino acids.

Texturised vegetable proteins (TVP) and mycoprotein are developed from plant proteins and are used by vegetarians and vegans. They can be produced as slices, chunks, mince, burgers and sausages. Both will take up the flavour of other foods they are being cooked with.

Fats

The main sources of fat in the Western diet come from animal and dairy products. These are called saturated fats and are solid at room temperature, for example butter, margarine and fat on meat, and they can contribute to heart disease. Plant fats are usually liquid at room temperature, for example olive and sunflower oils. They are known as unsaturated fats. They are less likely to contribute to heart disease, because they do not have the same effect of blocking the blood vessels as animal fats. Olive oil helps to protect against heart disease.

Essential fatty acids are very important in the prevention of heart disease. They are the Omega 3 and Omega 6 fatty acids. Omega 3 is found in oily fish, such as mackerel, sardines, fresh tuna (not tinned), salmon, pumpkin seeds, linseed, soya, walnuts and leafy green vegetables. Omega 6 fatty acids are found in sunflower, grape seed and corn oil as well as cereals, eggs and poultry.

Did you know?

If foods are mixed in the same meal, they will complement each other and become a complete protein, for example baked beans on toast. Bread is deficient in one essential amino acid and baked beans are deficient in another, so by eating them together, you can have a complete protein meal. Food combining is a way that vegetarians and vegans can obtain complete proteins in food without eating meat.

Did you know?

Fats have several important functions in the body:

- They are a concentrated source of energy in the diet.
- They help to provide insulation against the cold by preventing heat loss.
- They protect body organs, such as the kidneys.
- They help to transport and store vitamins A, D, E and K.
- They provide taste to food and make it easier to eat.

Remember

A healthy balanced diet should be made up of:

50–60 per cent carbohydrate

15 per cent protein

20–35 per cent fat (but no more than 10 per cent of that should be saturated).

Components of a balanced diet (2)

Essential nutrients

Vitamins and minerals are known as micronutrients because they are needed in quite small amounts, but they are nevertheless essential to health. You will learn about the main vitamins and minerals in this topic.

Activity	Dietary intake

Make a list of everything you have had to eat and drink in the past two days. With a partner, decide which food groups your food came from. When you have done this, join up with another pair and discuss the following:

1 Do you think your two-day food intake was balanced?

2 What did you eat too much of?

3 What could you have eaten more of?

Keep your list and notes of your discussion as you will need them later on.

Vitamins and minerals

Vitamins cannot be made by the body and they are essential to life. There are two types of vitamins: water-soluble and fat-soluble.

Water-soluble vitamins are the B vitamins and vitamin C. They cannot be stored in the body, so we must have a daily intake of foods containing them.

Table 6.1 Sources and functions of water-soluble vitamins.

Vitamin	Sources in diet	Function
B_1	Bread, nuts, cereals, flour, meat, eggs, potatoes, poultry, milk	Converts carbohydrate to glucose; helps digestion; aids correct functioning of nerves; required for building of blood; essential for growth.
B_2	Milk, liver, kidney, cereals, yeast, meat extract, eggs, cheese	Converts glucose to energy.
B_3	Meat extract, yeast extract, wholemeal bread, eggs, liver, cereals	Converts glucose to energy; maintains healthy skin and nervous system; required for cell metabolism.
B_5	Animal products, cereals, legumes	Converts glucose and fat to energy; maintains healthy immune system.
B_6	Meat, green vegetables, bran, wholemeal flour, eggs, bananas	Required for protein metabolism; converts tryptophan to niacin; essential for formation of haemoglobin.
B_9	Yeast, leafy green vegetables, meat, avocado, bananas	Produces red blood cells and tissue cells; required for normal growth; maintains healthy digestive tract.
B_{12}	Widely distributed in animal foods	Involved in manufacture of red blood cells in bone marrow; maintains nervous system.
C	Blackcurrants, citrus fruits, green vegetables, peppers, tomatoes	Required in formation of bones and teeth; essential in building of blood; required for wound healing; maintains immune system, and healthy skin and gums.

Vitamin names

As well as letters and numbers, water-soluble vitamins also have names. Carry out some research to find out these names.

Fat-soluble vitamins are A, D, E and K. They dissolve in fat in the body, which is why we need to consume fat in our diet. They are stored in the body in the liver.

Table 6.2 Sources and functions of fat-soluble vitamins.

Vitamin	Sources in diet	Function
A	Fish oil, liver, butter, cheese, eggs, milk, fruit and vegetables	Aids night vision; keeps skin and epithelial linings healthy.
D	Fish liver, oily fish, eggs, milk, margarine, sunlight	Required for absorption of calcium in intestine; regulates calcium and magnesium in bone tissue.
E	Eggs, cereal oils, vegetables, nuts, seeds	Maintains healthy muscular system; anti-oxidant; protects cell membranes.
K	Green vegetables, fish liver oils, alfalfa tablets, molasses, yoghurt	Essential for blood clotting.

Minerals

Minerals are also known as micronutrients because, like vitamins, they are only needed in very small amounts in the body. They are found in the earth and in the sea. They are necessary for many processes in the body and these are shown in the table below.

Table 6.3 Sources and functions of minerals.

Mineral	Sources in diet	Function
Calcium	Milk, cheese, bread, flour, seafood, nuts and green vegetables. For some, the bones in canned fish are important	Builds strong bones and hard teeth; essential for blood clotting; helps muscles and nerves to work; activates certain enzymes; requires vitamin D for absorption.
Sodium	Naturally in eggs, meat, vegetables, milk. Added to many processed foods, such as meat and canned food	Maintains body fluid balance and blood pressure; excess is linked to high blood pressure; aids muscle contraction and nerve transmission.
Iron	Meat (offal), bread, flour, cereal products, potatoes and vegetables	Needed by all cells; needed to form haemoglobin in red blood cells and myoglobin in muscles; absorbed by body relative to need; vitamin C increases absorption of iron.

Water

The human body is made up of about two-thirds water, and we cannot survive for more than a few days without it as it is needed for many processes. The European Food Safety Authority (EFSA) recommends that men have 2.5 litres a day and women 2 litres a day.

Take it further

Find out what the recommended daily allowance is for each of the vitamins and minerals in Tables 6.1 – 6.3. Make sure you use UK sources as there is variation in different countries.

Components of a balanced diet (3)

▼ The five food groups and their functions

As well as thinking of food as belonging to different nutrient groups, you can also think of different types of food. The Food Standards Agency identified the five different food groups in *The Balance of Good Health* (2001), and this information is given below.

Meat, fish and alternatives

This group is used in the body for growth and repair. It includes meat, poultry, fish, eggs, nuts, beans and pulses. Meat includes bacon and salami and meat products such as sausages, beefburgers and pâté. These are all quite high-fat choices. Beans and pulses are in this group and they are a good source of protein for vegetarians. Fish includes frozen and tinned fish, such as sardines and tuna, fish fingers and fishcakes. Aim to eat at least one portion of oily fish, such as sardines or salmon, each week. The main nutrients are iron, protein, B vitamins (especially B_{12}), zinc and magnesium.

The recommendation is to eat moderate amounts and choose lower-fat versions, such as meat with the fat cut off, poultry without the skin and fish without batter. Cook these foods without added fat. Beans and pulses are good alternatives to meat as they are naturally very low in fat.

Can you think of any more foods that belong to this group?

Fruit and vegetables

The main nutrients in fruit and vegetables are vitamin C, carotenes, folates, and some carbohydrate. They also provide fibre in the diet. Fresh, frozen and tinned fruit and vegetables, dried fruit and fruit juice are all included in this group. Beans and pulses can also be eaten.

The advice is to eat lots – at least five portions a day. Beans, pulses and fruit juice count as one portion, however much you eat or drink in a day. You should eat a wide variety of fruit and vegetables of as many different colours and types as possible. Try to avoid adding fat or rich sauces to vegetables (e.g. butter on potatoes), and sugar or syrupy dressings to fruit (e.g. chocolate sauce on banana).

How many portions of fruit and vegetables do you eat each day?

Bread, other cereals and potatoes

This group is mainly made up of carbohydrate-rich food and provides much of the energy needed in the diet. Other nutrients in them are calcium and iron, B vitamins and fibre. Cereals are foods such as breakfast cereals, pasta, rice, oats, noodles, maize, millet and cornmeal. This group also includes yams and plantains. Beans and pulses can be eaten as part of this group.

You should eat a lot of foods in this group, and try to eat wholemeal, wholegrain, brown or high-fibre versions where possible. Avoid having them fried too often and adding too much fat (e.g. thickly spread butter, margarine or low-fat spread on bread), or adding rich sauces to pasta.

How many foods can you name in this group?

Milk and dairy foods

This food group includes milk, cheese, yoghurt and fromage frais, but not butter and cream. The main nutrients are calcium, protein, vitamins A, B_{12} and D. They are needed in the body to build strong bones and teeth and maintain healthy skin and eyes. The recommendation is to eat or drink moderate amounts, and choose lower-fat versions whenever you can.

Lower-fat versions mean semi-skimmed or skimmed milk, low fat (0.1 per cent fat) yoghurts or fromage frais, and lower-fat cheeses. Check the amount of fat by looking at the information on the labels. Compare similar products and choose the lowest; for example, 8 per cent fromage frais may be labelled 'low fat', but it is not actually the lowest available.

What are your favourite dairy products?

Foods containing fat/foods and drinks containing sugar

Foods containing fat include margarine, butter, other spreading fats and low-fat spreads, cooking oils, oil-based salad dressings, mayonnaise, cream, chocolate, crisps, biscuits, pastries, cakes, puddings, ice cream, rich sauces and gravies.

Foods containing sugar include soft drinks, sweets, jam and sugar, as well as foods such as cakes, puddings, biscuits, pastries and ice cream.

The main nutrients are fats, including some essential fatty acids, and fat is needed in the body to transport vitamins A, D, E and K, which are the fat-soluble vitamins. Some products also contain salt or sugar. Sugar is described by some people as 'empty calories', because it contains calories, but few, if any, nutrients.

You should eat foods containing fat sparingly and look out for low-fat alternatives. Foods and drinks containing sugar should not be consumed too often as they can contribute to tooth decay.

All foods and drinks containing sugar should be consumed mainly at mealtimes to reduce the risk of tooth decay.

Can you think of any healthy alternatives to your favourite snacks?

Components of a balanced diet (4)

Recommended Daily Intakes (RDIs)

A balanced diet will depend on the types of food you eat and your nutritional needs. The wider the variety of foods eaten, the more nutrients you will get from them. It is now known that some health problems are caused by dietary intake, such as too much fat causing heart disease and too much salt contributing to strokes.

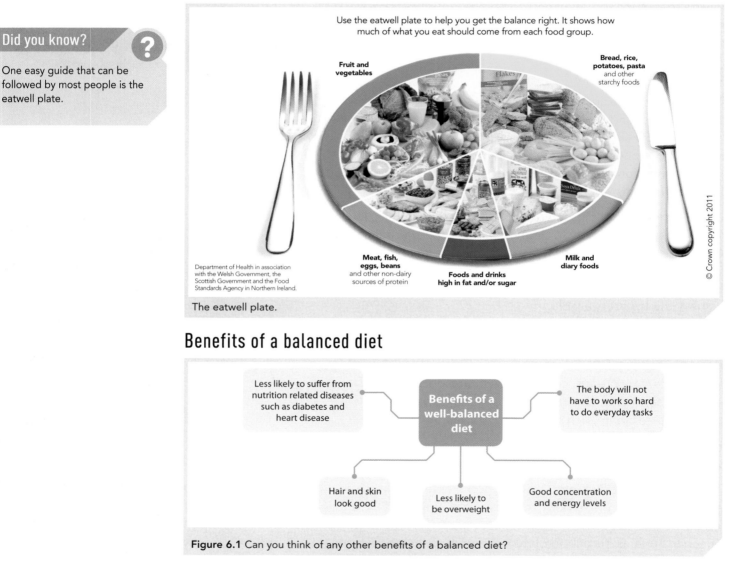

The eatwell plate.

Benefits of a balanced diet

Less likely to suffer from nutrition related diseases such as diabetes and heart disease

Benefits of a well-balanced diet

The body will not have to work so hard to do everyday tasks

Hair and skin look good

Less likely to be overweight

Good concentration and energy levels

Figure 6.1 Can you think of any other benefits of a balanced diet?

Intake and needs

People have different dietary needs and intake depending on a range of factors:

- Height, weight and gender
- The level of exercise taken
- The type of job a person does
- Likes and dislikes
- A person's health
- Availability of food.

Are there any other factors that would determine what and how much a person needs to eat?

Dietary reference values

There are a variety of dietary reference values that can be used to identify different nutritional requirements for people of different ages and needs. They are shown in Table 6.4.

Table 6.4 Dietary reference values.

Dietary reference value	Definition
Estimated Average Requirement (EAR)	An estimate of the average need for food energy or a nutrient. Some people will need more than this average and some will need less.
Reference Nutrient Intake (RNI)	The amount of a nutrient that is enough for almost every individual, even those with high needs. The RNI is generally much higher than most people need. The RNI supplies enough of a nutrient for at least 97.5% of the population.
Lower Reference Nutrient Intake (LRNI)	The amount of a nutrient considered to be sufficient for the small number of individuals with low nutrient needs (only about 2.5% of the population).

In 2011, the Scientific Advisory Committee on Nutrition (SACN) published new guidelines on Estimated Average Requirements for the UK population. This is the average amount that individuals of average weight should consume. Table 6.5 shows the requirements in both megajoules and kilocalories.

Table 6.6 shows the recommended daily intakes for some common nutrients.

Table 6.6 Recommended daily intakes for common nutrients.

	Boys 11–14	Girls 11–14	Men 19–50	Women 19–50
Protein (g)	42.1	41.2	55.5	45
Calcium (mg)	1000	800	700	700
Iron (mg)	11.3	14.8	8.7	14.8
Zinc (mg)	9	9	9.5	7
Vitamin C (mg)	35	35	40	40

Source: DEFRA Manual of Nutrition, 12th Edition 2012.

Table 6.5 Estimated Average Requirements.

Age (years)	Estimated Average Requirement	
	MJ/day (Kcal/day)	
	Males	Females
1	3.2 (765)	3.0 (717)
5	6.2 (1482)	5.7 (1362)
10	8.5 (2032)	8.1 (1936)
16	12.4 (2964)	10.1 (2414)
18	13.2 (3155)	10.3 (2462)
19–24	11.6 (2772)	9.1 (2175)
25–34	11.5 (2749)	9.1 (2175)
35–44	11.0 (2629)	8.8 (2013)
45–54	10.8 (2581)	8.8 (2013)
55–64	10.8 (2581)	8.7 (2079)
65–74	9.8 (2342)	8.0 (1912)
75+	9.6 (2294)	7.7 (1840)

Source: SACN Dietary Reference Values for Energy, 2011.

Activity	Recommended daily intakes

Use the tables above to answer the following:

1 At what age are male and female energy needs greatest?

2 Explain why girls' and women's iron requirements are higher than boys' and men's.

3 Why is a male's protein requirement higher than a female's?

Long-term effects of a balanced diet

What is a balanced diet?

A balanced diet helps to maintain a healthy body. If you eat the right foods in the right amounts, you should be the right weight for your height and not have too much body fat. This means that your body will work efficiently, you will feel happy and you will be less prone to diseases, such as diabetes, heart disease and cancer. The eatwell plate shows the recommended amounts of each food group that should be eaten. It is also important to keep an eye on portion sizes.

Another recommendation is to keep to the 80/20 rule. If you eat healthily 80 per cent of the time, you can eat less healthy foods 20 per cent of the time with little ill effect.

Raised immunity to infections

The body's immune system helps to protect against disease. Fresh fruit and vegetables which contain vitamins A and E, and foods such as garlic and honey can help to maintain a healthy immune system. Foods high in zinc and omega-3 fatty acids also boost the immune system.

Greater energy levels

People who are overweight often have low energy levels. This is because they have to use up a lot of energy just to do a basic level of exercise, and have little or no energy to do more. Although we need to eat carbohydrates to give us the energy we need, it's important to make sure we don't eat too many, and get most of our energy from complex carbohydrates with a high fibre content. Getting into the habit of eating healthily will boost energy levels.

Having energy to exercise will boost your health and wellbeing.

Increased concentration

Research shows that children who eat breakfast have better concentration levels and do better at school than those who don't. Some believe that too many carbohydrates can lower concentration levels. Behaviour is also improved through a balanced diet. Studies carried out at the University of Southampton showed that children who had drinks with high amounts of additives were less able to concentrate and were more hyperactive than those who didn't.

Which drinks would you recommend to these children to help them concentrate?

Faster healing of skin, tissues and mucus membranes

A diet that is rich in vitamins A, C and E aids the healing of the skin, tissues and mucus membranes. Vitamin C in particular helps to form connective tissue in cuts. It also assists in making red blood cells and fighting infection, especially colds. Vitamin E helps to make less scar tissue and break down blood clots.

Did you know?

The Balance of Good Health is based on the Government's Eight Guidelines for a Healthy Diet. It forms the basis of the Food Standards Agency Nutrition Strategy. If people follow the recommended amounts and make sure that they choose different foods, this should ensure that they have a balanced diet.

The Government's Eight Guidelines are:

- Base your meals on starchy foods.
- Eat lots of fruit and vegetables.
- Eat more fish.
- Cut down on saturated fat and sugar.
- Eat less salt – no more than 6g a day.
- Get active and try to be a healthy weight.
- Drink plenty of water.
- Don't skip breakfast.

Long-term effects of an unbalanced diet (1)

▶ Malnutrition

Malnutrition can take different forms: too much nutritional intake can result in over-nutrition and obesity, and too little nutritional intake can result in under-nutrition or starvation.

Over-nutrition

Coronary heart disease – This can occur through eating too many animal proteins that are high in saturated fats. To maintain a healthy heart, people are advised to eat two to three meals containing oily fish such as salmon, mackerel, sardines or fresh tuna (not tinned) per week, and plenty of fresh fruit and vegetables. Regular exercise that raises the heart rate and maintaining a healthy weight will help to prevent this.

Weight gain and obesity – Any food that is eaten in excess will be converted to fat and stored in the body, which leads to weight gain and obesity. A healthy balanced diet together with exercise will help people to lose weight. Maintaining the correct weight for your height might require a lifestyle change, such as changing what you eat and taking regular exercise.

Type 2 diabetes – This is also known as late or adult onset diabetes, but it is seen today in children as young as nine years old. It is caused by eating too much fat and sugar. The pancreas is either unable to produce enough insulin for the cells to absorb glucose from the blood, or the body becomes resistant to the insulin that is produced. Symptoms of type 2 diabetes include thirst, excessive urination and extreme tiredness. It can be controlled by diet alone, or by diet and medication. Type 2 diabetics do not normally need insulin.

Stroke – A stroke occurs when brain cells die because the oxygen supply has been interrupted or stopped. Strokes are often caused by high blood pressure and one of the main causes of this is eating too much salt, but obesity and lack of exercise can also contribute to high blood pressure.

Under-nutrition

Specific nutrient **deficiencies** – This can result from a general lack of nutrients or a particular nutrient. It is not often seen in developed countries, but can be common in developing countries.

Diets low in thiamin (vitamin B_1) and magnesium may also cause low concentration span. A diet rich in fruit and vegetables, fatty acids, bread and meat will help poor concentration and behavioural problems.

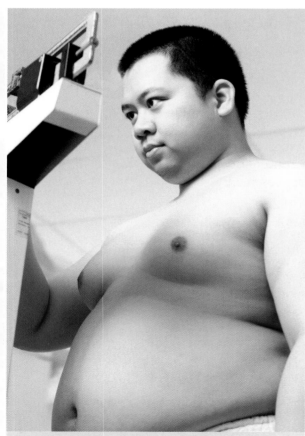

Why is it important to encourage healthy eating from a young age?

A vegetarian diet is usually high in fibre and low in fat and this makes it a healthy diet. As long as vegetarians are aware of the need to combine vegetable-based foods to make **high biological value proteins**, they can get all the nutrients they need.

Vegans can suffer from vitamin B_{12} deficiency as this is mainly found in animal products, although yeast extract is a good source, and provided vegans know about healthy eating choices, they can obtain everything they need from this diet. Nutritionists tend to advise that a vegan diet is not suitable for young children because it contains so much bulk that is filling that they may not eat enough to get the energy they need. However, a vegan diet containing a wide variety of foods will allow children to grow and develop normally, although they are likely to be lighter and leaner than meat-eating children.

Key terms

Malnutrition – lack of proper nutrition, caused by not having enough to eat, not eating enough of the right things, or being unable to use the food that one does eat.

Deficiency – a lack of a nutrient that is necessary.

High biological protein – a protein that provides the body with all eight essential amino acids.

Assessment activity 6.1

2A.P1 | 2A.P2 | 2A.M1 | 2A.D1

You have a part-time job at a local leisure centre and the manager is planning a 'get healthy week' for the people who use the facilities. There will be a variety of activities, including presentations and taster sessions. The manager wants you to help him prepare a booklet about balanced diets to be available for people to take home.

1 Using the information you have learned so far and carrying out further research, start your booklet by providing a table identifying and describing the components of a balanced diet and their functions, sources and effects on the body.

2 Create an eye-catching page that describes the effects of an unbalanced diet. Make sure that you link these effects to the causes: for example, a stroke is caused by high blood pressure due to a high salt intake.

3 Compare the effects of balanced and unbalanced diets on the health and wellbeing of individuals. Provide two case studies, one about someone who has a balanced diet and the other about someone who has an unbalanced diet, describing the effects of each and comparing them. Include an assessment of the long-term effects of a balanced and unbalanced diet on the health and wellbeing of individuals.

Tips

Remember that an unbalanced diet may include too much of some nutrients and not enough of others.

You need to make sure that the handout and leaflet that you provide is user-friendly, and that anyone who reads it can understand the information.

You must think carefully about the two people in your case studies. You may choose to use real people, but if you do, make sure you maintain confidentiality.

Long-term effects of an unbalanced diet (2)

▼ Vitamin deficiency

Although it is possible to become deficient in vitamins, in the UK it is rare as many foods are fortified with vitamins to prevent deficiency diseases occurring. However, in developing countries some vitamin deficiency diseases can be fatal, especially in children.

Table 6.7 Effects of vitamin deficiency.

Vitamin	Effect of shortage
A	Night blindness (also known as xeropthalmia or dry eye). In its early stages, it can be cured by providing sufferers with vitamin A supplements such as palm oil or other foods high in vitamin A. However, in its later stages it is incurable and leads to complete blindness and in some cases death. Vitamin A deficiency can also cause itching, thickening of horny layer of the skin, ageing of the skin, dry skin and loss of taste.
B_1 (thiamin)	Beriberi, causing some or all of the following: neuritis (inflammation of the nerves), headache, fatigue, poor memory, diarrhoea, anxiety, insomnia, depression, irritability, eczema, dermatitis, acne, enlarged heart, muscle weakness, wrist and ankle drop, poor appetite, tenderness in calf muscles and pins and needles in legs.
B_2 (riboflavin)	Chapping of the lips, cracking at the corner of the mouth, soreness of the tongue, sensitivity to light, and skin rashes. It may also cause red, itchy eyes, night blindness, cataracts, migraines, peripheral neuropathy, anaemia and tiredness. There can also be some abnormalities associated with development, e.g. cleft lip and palate, growth problems and congenital heart defects.
B_3	Pellagra, causing redness of skin, exfoliation of hands and face, weakness, diarrhoea, memory loss, irritability and insomnia. Deficiency is rare and if supplements are needed, they should be given under medical supervision.
B_5	Weakness, depression, lowered resistance to infection, numbness, muscle cramps, restlessness, sleep disturbances, nausea, vomiting and abdominal cramps. Deficiency is very rare.
B_6	Anaemia, fatigue, nerve dysfunction, sore tongue, skin inflammation and depression.
B_9	Megaloblastic anaemia (abnormally large red blood cells), neural tube defects (e.g. spina bifida), nausea and headaches, memory loss, depression, loss of appetite and diarrhoea.
B_{12}	Pernicious anaemia, tiredness, loss of appetite, weight loss, breathlessness, diarrhoea, red and sore tongue, degeneration of nerve cells, a change in taste, ringing in the ears (tinnitus).
C	Scurvy, bleeding gums and loose teeth, incomplete cell repair, easy bruising, tiredness, and physical and mental stress.
D	Rickets, causing osteomalacia, spontaneous fractures, obesity, overactive parathyroid hormones, depression and fatigue.
E	Slow healing, poor muscle, circulatory and nerve performance. Vitamin E deficiency as a result of diet is rare.
K	Problems with blood clotting. It is very rare, but occasionally babies need a supplement at birth.

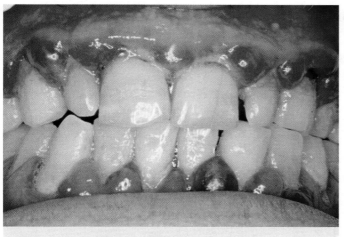

Bleeding gums are one of the symptoms of scurvy.

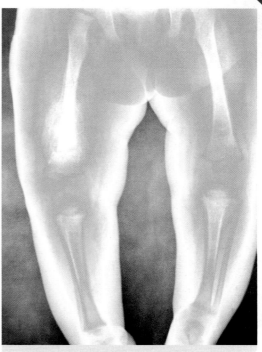

An X-ray of the bones of a person with rickets.

Mineral deficiency

Calcium

Osteoporosis is caused by loss of bone density. People with this condition are at greater risk of fracturing bones, especially wrists, hips and vertebrae. Any activity that promotes stronger bones will help to prevent osteoporosis, so walking and running are good. Calcium-rich foods, such as cheese, milk, bread and tinned fish should be included in the diet. It is important also to have enough vitamin D as calcium cannot be absorbed without it.

Iron

Iron deficiency is known as **anaemia**. Iron is required in the formation of healthy red blood cells, and helps the body to use oxygen efficiently. Symptoms of anaemia include fatigue, brittle fingernails, weakness and lack of energy. Asian people may become anaemic as they have a diet low in iron. Teenage girls are sometimes anaemic due to blood loss from starting menstruation. It can be easily treated by taking iron supplements and eating iron-rich foods, such as red meat and dark green leafy vegetables.

Nutrient excess

Tooth decay, which is also known as **dental caries,** is caused by an excess of sugar in the diet. Bacteria, food and saliva combine and form sticky deposits (**plaque**) which are deposited on the teeth. Plaque is acid and over time it will dissolve the enamel on teeth, causing cavities. If they remain untreated, they can kill the tooth's nerve and blood supply and eventually the whole tooth will die. Sugary foods and drinks should be kept to a minimum and good dental hygiene observed.

? Did you know?

You should follow these tips for looking after your teeth:

- Brush your teeth twice a day, in the morning and in the evening.
- Spend at least three minutes each time.
- Always use a fluoride toothpaste.
- Use a small toothbrush so that you can reach the back teeth, applying no more than a pea-sized amount of toothpaste for adults.
- Flossing is very important as the toothbrush does not always reach the gaps between the teeth.
- Do not brush too hard – this can damage gums.
- Limit your consumption of sugar and starchy foods.
- Visit your dentist regularly.

Source: NHS Choices

Factors influencing the diet of individuals and their associated dietary needs (1)

Getting started ⏩

In small groups, discuss what you all eat with your family. Are there differences in what you eat, and if there are, why? Is it to do with religion or culture, health, or just likes and dislikes? Show the results of your discussion as a picture or series of pictures.

Introduction

Although nutritionists and dieticians give advice to people about healthy eating and devise diets for people with particular conditions, they have to take other factors into consideration. There are many different factors that will influence what people eat, and you will explore them in this topic.

▶ Religion and culture

Hinduism

Although some Hindus are vegetarian, many are not. Most avoid beef as the cow is seen as sacred in their religion, and some avoid eggs. Hindus who do not eat beef will also avoid cheese and yoghurt containing rennet as it is produced from cows. Strict Hindus avoid mushrooms, garlic, onions, tea and coffee (containing caffeine), and alcohol. Some Hindus will fast at times of special festivals.

An example of Kosher foods.

Judaism

Jewish people generally eat **kosher** foods. This means that they do not eat pork, and will only eat other meat where the animal has been killed according to kosher laws. They eat fish, but not shellfish, such as prawns, mussels and scallops. Orthodox Jews do not mix meat and milk products in the same meal, so would not have a cheeseburger or lasagne, for example. According to household custom, they would wait one, three or six hours to eat a dairy product after eating meat. Yom Kippur or the Day of Atonement is the holiest day in the Jewish calendar and traditionally requires Jews to fast for 25 hours. Children under the age of nine are not allowed to fast, nor are people who are pregnant or in poor health.

Islam

Muslims usually eat lawful or halal foods. This is similar to kosher in the Jewish faith, in that animals for meat must be slaughtered according to religious law. Unlawful or haram food includes pork and pork products, but cheese, fish and shellfish are halal foods. Alcohol is unlawful to Muslims, and some choose not to drink caffeinated drinks. Fasting takes place during Ramadan, the Muslim holy month, for 30 days. During this time, no food or drink may be eaten between sunrise and sunset.

Buddhism

There are no set dietary laws in Buddhism. Although most Buddhists are either vegetarian or vegan, some will eat meat and/or fish. Some avoid onion, garlic and leeks, but dietary choice depends on what branch of Buddhism is studied and in which country. Strict Buddhists do not drink alcohol.

◤ Moral reasons

Some people choose to follow a particular diet for moral reasons, rather than religious beliefs or particular customs.

Vegetarians

Some people don't eat meat and fish because they don't like the taste or texture, they disapprove of the way that animals are reared, or the way that animals and fish are killed.

There are different types of vegetarian:

Table 6.8 Different types of vegetarian.

Vegetarian type	Diet
Semi- or demi-vegetarian	No red meat, but will eat fish and poultry
Lacto-vegetarian	Dairy such as yoghurt, milk and cheese, but not eggs, meat, fish or poultry
Ovo-vegetarian	Eggs, but not dairy, meat, fish or poultry
Lacto-ovo-vegetarian	Dairy products and eggs, but not meat, fish or poultry

Internationally recognised symbols for kosher and halal foods.

Restaurant menus use a green 'V' to indicate vegetarian dishes, and labels on packaged foods are sometimes marked in the same way to show that the product is suitable for vegetarians.

Vegans

Veganism is a stricter form of vegetarianism, and vegans eat no animal foods at all. Many refuse to wear leather or wool goods as well. Vegetarians and vegans must combine different plant proteins in meals to ensure that they get enough protein in their diets.

Activity	Vegetarian and vegan food

Do some online research on vegetarian and vegan foods and recipes.

Produce a handout or booklet with recipes for one breakfast, lunch and dinner for a lacto-ovo-vegetarian and one for a vegan. Make sure that the meals are balanced and that you have combined the food to ensure that there is sufficient protein.

Factors influencing the diet of individuals and their associated dietary needs (2)

Environment

Access to food and food storage

In developed countries, people have access to a good variety of food which can come from all over the world, and the increase in air travel means that most foods are available all year round. For the population of developed countries, this can lead to over-nutrition. The longer fruit and vegetables are stored, the more nutrients they lose. In developing countries, people often have access to restricted diets that are high in carbohydrates and not so rich in protein and fats. This can lead to under-nutrition.

Location

Where you live will have an effect on your diet. Although there is enough food in the world, it is not evenly distributed. More wealthy countries can afford to buy food and so have a greater variety than countries that are poor. Food that is grown in poor soil will contain fewer minerals and so the quality of the diet will be poorer.

Climate

Many developing countries suffer from poor soil conditions, flooding and drought, which result in repeated years of lost harvests. In 1995 and 1996, severe flooding in North Korea destroyed crops and the harvest, including the reserve grain stores that were being stored underground. As a result, many people starved to death.

Socio-economic factors

Costs

The cost of food varies according to the region of the country where people live and the type of shop that sells it. Changes in the economy also have an effect, and the financial status of the country affects cost. Large chain supermarkets sell in large quantities, which means that they can sell at a lower price than independent shops that have much less space and stock.

Income

The ability to afford food is linked to social class. People who are in higher social classes have more money to spend on food and tend to buy better-quality food, and eat out more. People who have low incomes are more likely to buy food that is high in salt, fat, and sugar and provides concentrated sources of energy to help them feel fuller for longer.

A fast food snack.

Trends

Just as you might follow trends, such as wearing clothes that are in fashion, or downloading the same music or apps as your friends, some people follow trends in eating. In recent years there has been an increase in the number of bio yoghurts on sale that claim to strengthen the body's defences or aid digestion.

Family

There is not much evidence to suggest that there is a difference in food choice depending on an individual's position in the family, but it is known that mothers will often give more protein or fruit and vegetables, or larger quantities to their husband/partner or children. They will then fill up on lower-quality food and their nutritional status may suffer.

Class

There is some evidence that differences in social class influence dietary choices. In general, people from the upper social classes eat more healthy food, and poorer people eat less fruit and vegetables and more high-fat, high-sugar foods. Women in the lower social classes are more likely to be obese than women in the upper social classes. People in lower social classes usually earn less money than those in the higher social classes and are more likely to substitute cheap processed food for fresh food.

Peer pressure

Peer pressure can have an effect on the food choices that are made, especially by children and teenagers. Many young people develop a stereotypical view of people who eat healthy and unhealthy food and may choose less healthy options to copy their friends.

The media

Information in the media can influence food choice. Food scares can be caused by what is reported in the press. In 2006, products were recalled after there was a salmonella scare in a chocolate factory. More recently, there has been a lot of publicity about rising levels of obesity in the UK.

◤ Personal preferences

Although some people like almost everything that is put in front of them, there are others who only eat food they really enjoy. Often in a family household, the food is mainly chosen and cooked by one person, so their preferences may be dominant. However, as long as healthy eating guidelines are followed, the diet will be balanced. It is less easy to ensure a child has a balanced diet if they are fussy, and parents often need to come up with imaginative ways to make their children eat.

Factors influencing the diet of individuals and their associated dietary needs (3)

Illness

Effects on appetite and dietary requirements

How do you feel when you are ill? When we feel really unwell, we often lose our appetite until we start to feel better. Some conditions can increase appetite, such as an overactive thyroid gland.

Some illnesses may affect the body so that the food eaten can't be digested, and in some cases treatment for illness will affect dietary intake. People who have a poor appetite should be encouraged to eat small amounts of food which are high in nutrients, and it is well known that vitamins and minerals are necessary for health and healing.

Activity	Effects on appetite

Carry out some research into the causes of both loss of appetite and increased appetite. What other conditions may affect appetite?

An EpiPen: an instrument for giving medication for severe allergic reactions that people can use on themselves.

Underlying health conditions

Allergies

Do you have an allergy to peanuts, prawns or strawberries? Many people do. Allergic reactions to food vary in intensity. Similar symptoms and illnesses can be triggered by different allergens, yet the same allergens can also cause very different reactions in different people. Symptoms can include eczema, asthma, urticaria (hives) and other health problems. Anaphylaxis is an extreme reaction which must be treated by adrenaline injections. Failure to treat this promptly can result in death. Avoidance of food that causes allergies is the only way to prevent the onset of symptoms, although some people have desensitisation treatment which can be very effective.

Lactose intolerance

Lactose intolerance is an inability to digest lactose, the sugar found in milk and milk products. It is particularly common in people of African, Asian and Indian races and can lead to digestive disturbance, such as cramps, diarrhoea and wind. Milk should be avoided in the diet, but often sufferers can tolerate yoghurt and cheese because the lactose is converted to lactic acid during manufacture.

Coeliac disease

Coeliac disease is an autoimmune disease caused by the protein gluten, which is found in wheat, barley and rye. Symptoms include abdominal pain, cramping and bloating, nausea and vomiting, and diarrhoea. People with this condition should avoid foods containing gluten. This is quite difficult because many foods contain thickeners made of gluten, so people with the condition tend to become experts in reading food labels.

Diabetes

People who suffer from type 2 diabetes can help the levels of blood glucose by maintaining a diet low in fat and sugar. Complex carbohydrates should form a part of the diet, as low carbohydrate diets can be high in fat. There is a relatively high incidence of coronary heart disease in diabetics in the United Kingdom.

Why is it important to regularly test the blood sugar level of diabetic patients?

Crohn's disease

The cause of Crohn's disease is unknown, but it is a chronic inflammatory condition that affects the whole of the digestive tract. Symptoms include abdominal pain, diarrhoea, weight loss, fever and tiredness. Sufferers of the disease can go into remission and have no symptoms at times. Crohn's disease is treated by diet, usually an individual diet plan for each person.

Irritable bowel syndrome (IBS)

The cause of IBS is not known, but triggers may be stress or immune system problems. It usually affects people in their twenties and thirties. Symptoms include stomach cramps, bloating, diarrhoea and constipation. There is no cure, but changing diet and lifestyle can help.

Nutritional variation during life stage development (1)

Introduction

A person's diet changes during his or her lifespan, according to need and the ability of the body to digest the food. Although we all need the same macro- and micronutrients, we need them in different quantities and different formats at different stages in our lives.

Life stages

Infancy (0–2 years)

Weaning can help babies develop social skills.

From birth, breast milk contains all the baby's needs in the right amounts. Although it is low in iron and copper, the baby has enough of these stored until it starts eating solid foods at about six months. Breast milk is clean, provides immunity and does not have to be prepared. Some mothers can't or choose not to breastfeed and use formula milk, which is modified cow's milk. It must be made up according to the instructions provided to prevent damage to the baby's immature kidneys, and equipment must be sterilised to prevent infection. **Weaning** too early may cause obesity or allergies later.

Table 6.9 shows when different foods should be introduced. Mothers may find that they need to introduce foods several times before the baby gets used to the taste and texture. This can help to prevent children becoming fussy eaters.

Table 6.9 The weaning process.

Age	Weaning process
6 months	Start with spoonfuls of baby rice, mashed potato or puréed vegetables, such as carrot, peas or parsnips. When they are used to the spoon, introduce lots of tastes, such as puréed meat, pulses and fruit.
	As a baby gets used to eating, introduce food with soft lumps. Do not give nuts as infants may choke or be allergic to them.
9 months	Minced or finely chopped food can be given. Infants at this age should be given different textures to get them used to them.
12 months	Give a good mixed diet by this stage, including three meals and two to three healthy snacks each day.

Key terms

Weaning – introduction of solid food into the baby's diet from about six months of age.

Activity   Weaning

Use the internet to research weaning. Find out at what stage different foods should be introduced and produce a handout for new mums on weaning.

Childhood (3–8 years)

Children aged between three and eight years of age tend to be very active and are growing fast. Although their energy requirements are not as high as those of adults, they need almost the same amount of some vitamins and minerals.

Some children have big appetites because they have high nutritional needs. Children should be encouraged to eat healthy meals consisting of a mix of meat, fish or eggs and potatoes, pasta or rice with vegetables.

Table 6.10 Daily energy needs of babies and children.

Age range	Male		Female	
	MJ	Kcal	MJ	Kcal
1-2 months (Breast milk substitute-fed)	2.5	598	2.3	550
3 – 4 months	2.6	622	2.5	598
5 - 6 months	2.7	646	2.6	622
7 - 12 months	3.1	742	2.8	670
3 years	4.9	1171	4.5	1076
6 years	6.6	1577	6.2	1482
9 years	7.7	1840	7.2	1721
12 years	9.4	2247	8.8	2103

Source: DEFRA, *Manual of Nutrition*, 12th Edition, 2012

Adolescence (9–18 years)

The nutritional needs of adolescents are greater than for any other age group because they have large appetites and are still growing. Boys aged 11 to 14 need approximately 2,354 kilocalories a day, rising to 3,005 for 15 to 18 year olds. Girls need 2,175 and 2,432 kilocalories respectively. Adolescents should be encouraged to eat sensibly and healthily at regular intervals and to avoid phases of overeating or starving themselves in order to lose weight, and to take a regular amount of physical activity.

Both children and adolescents should avoid too many sweets, crisps, biscuits and fizzy drinks.

Activity   Healthy eating for children

Visit the Change4life website and find out what advice there is for encouraging children to eat healthy meals. You can access this by going to www.pearsonhotlinks.co.uk and searching for this title.

Make a poster for 7 to 10 year olds that gives them advice on making healthy food choices.

Nutritional variation during life stage development (2)

Introduction

Although our nutritional needs do not change a lot during adulthood, as we age our bodies can become less active and efficient. As a result, we need to make sure that we know how to maintain a healthy and balanced diet to suit our needs. Intake that is more than the amount of energy we expend will cause weight gain, and less activity can also result in weight gain, weakened bones and muscles, and loss of ability.

Early to middle adulthood (19 to 65 years)

An adult's nutritional needs reduce with age. Men and women between 19 and 45 need approximately 2,550 and 1,940 kilocalories per day, but this will vary with the amount of activity or exercise taken. In general, adults need to eat a healthy diet consisting of complex carbohydrates, such as bread, potatoes, rice or pasta, protein, such as meat, eggs, cheese or fish and at least five daily portions of fruit and vegetables. Foods with high levels of fat, particularly saturated fat, and sugar should be kept to a minimum and adults are advised to carry out physical activity on a regular basis. Alcohol intake should be limited as it contributes extra calories to the diet.

Between the ages of 45 and 64 men need between 2,550 and 2,380 kilocalories per day and women 1,900. They should have at least five portions of fruit and vegetables a day to provide vitamins, minerals, fibre and water, which will help to prevent constipation. Osteoporosis can be a problem for older people, particularly women, so calcium-rich foods should be included in the diet, although they should be advised to stick to low-fat versions where possible. Walking and any exercise that is considered to be weight-bearing will help to strengthen bones too. A couple of meals a week containing oily fish, such as salmon, mackerel or sardines will help to protect against heart disease.

Pregnancy and breastfeeding

During pregnancy and breastfeeding a woman's nutritional needs are increased to provide nutrition for the growing baby and for making breast milk after the baby is born. Pregnant women are advised to avoid eating foods high in vitamin A, soft cheeses and patés which may contain listeria bacteria, as they can cause birth defects.

Although some people think that being pregnant means that a woman can 'eat for two', only about an extra 200 kilocalories a day are required in the last three months of the pregnancy, and about

Why is it important for pregnant women to have a balanced diet?

450 to 570 kilocalories a day extra during breastfeeding. This is to give the mother the energy she needs to carry the extra weight of the baby and to make breast milk. Women planning to become pregnant should be advised to eat a diet rich in folic acid to prevent damage to the foetus, particularly spina bifida.

Later adulthood (65+)

Although there is not much difference in the dietary needs of adults and older adults, as we age we become less mobile and we need less energy for our daily needs. Men and women between the ages of 65 and 73 need approximately 2,330 and 1,990 calories a day. Over the age of 75, they need 2,100 and 1,810 kilocalories a day respectively. Older people have smaller appetites, so the diet should provide concentrated sources of protein, vitamins and minerals in smaller portions. Gentle exercise should also be encouraged.

In old age, the body begins to slow down and does not work as efficiently as in younger days, so older people are more likely to become constipated. They should be encouraged to drink plenty, and to have at least five portions of fruit and vegetables a day. Taste sensation can alter in old age, which might make food seem tasteless and unappetising. Strong flavours, such as herbs and spices, can be used to improve taste and might encourage older people to eat more.

Old people who live alone often cannot be bothered to cook a hot meal for one person, so they should be encouraged to eat foods that do not require much preparation but are high in nutrients. It is a good idea for older people to make sure that they have some tinned or dried food in the cupboard and some longlife milk, in case of illness or bad weather.

There are some companies that provide ready-made meals that can be delivered frozen and a microwave oven to heat the food, but this might be too expensive an option for some elderly people. In some areas of the country, there are 'meals on wheels' services that deliver a hot meal once a day to older people.

? Think about it

Malnutrition in older people can be caused by poor-fitting dentures or bad teeth. Why do you think this is?

Hot food served at a day care setting may help vulnerable people meet their nutritional needs.

Considerations for nutritional planning

Introduction

There are times when healthcare professionals may see patients who need dietary advice, whether it is just to lose weight, or to help in the treatment of an illness or disease.

A dietician or nutritionist normally provides a dietary plan for an individual on a long-term basis, but other healthcare workers can do so provided they have a sound knowledge and understanding of dietary intake, the long-term effects of balanced and unbalanced diets, and specific dietary needs of individuals at different life stages.

When planning suitable diets, it is important to get to know the individual and their eating habits, as many factors need to be considered.

A nutritional plan can then be put together taking into account as much of the information gathered as possible. An example of a one-week plan is shown in Table 6.11.

Jack is a 57-year-old sales executive who has had a heart attack. He has just been discharged from hospital following treatment and has been given a diet plan by Anoushka, the dietician. This is to be combined with taking regular exercise and drinking one to two litres of water a day.

You will see that there are three meals which include oily fish (tinned tuna is not included) and there are at least five portions of fruit and vegetables every day. There are a couple of treats as Jack is likely to be bored with this diet long term, and provided he sticks to the plan, he should remain healthy.

Assessment activity 6.2 — *English* — 2B.P3 | 2B.P4 | 2B.M2 | 2B.M3 | 2B.D2

As trainee dietician, you are working with a dietician in a GP practice. She runs a training session every two months for the doctors, nurses and healthcare assistants at the practice. She asks you to prepare a PowerPoint presentation for use at the next teaching session about individuals with specific dietary needs. She has given you two sets of patient notes and has asked you to make a sample nutritional plan for each patient:

- Sarah is a 22-year-old Jewish mother of two who is pregnant with her third child. Her husband has just been made redundant.
- Alan is a 45-year-old bank manager who is married to Helena, and they have grown-up children who no longer live at home. They are both vegan, and Alan runs about six marathons a year and trains every day.

1 Describe the specific nutritional needs for Sarah and Alan.

2 Explain the different factors that influence the diets of Sarah and Alan.

3 Discuss how the different factors will influence the diets of Sarah and Alan.

4 Show your nutritional plans for Sarah and Alan to the group, and compare them. You might want to create a handout showing the nutritional plans in detail.

Tips

You have been given the main points about the lifestyles of Sarah and Alan, but you can introduce more information that can be used to add further detail to your presentation. Make sure that it is realistic, so set aside enough time for research and preparation.

Table 6.11 An example diet plan.

	Breakfast	Snack	Lunch	Snack	Dinner
Sunday	Porridge made with skimmed milk and dried fruit Tea with skimmed milk	Banana Coffee with skimmed milk	Sandwich made with lean ham, salad and low-fat mayo Six cherry tomatoes Tea with skimmed milk	Low fat yoghurt Tea with skimmed milk	Roast chicken Dry roasted potatoes Carrots Cabbage Gravy Small portion of apple crumble, custard One glass of red wine
Monday	Two slices of wholemeal toast Low fat spread Marmite Tea with skimmed milk Orange juice	Two plums Coffee with skimmed milk	Jacket potato with tuna and sweetcorn (low-fat mayonnaise)	Two water biscuits with a small portion of reduced-fat cheese Celery	Vegetable curry Rice Low-fat chocolate mousse
Tuesday	Two poached eggs Two rashers of grilled bacon, fat removed Orange juice Tea with skimmed milk	Carrot and celery sticks Can of diet cola	Small can baked beans Two slices of wholemeal toast, no spread Water	Tea with skimmed milk Two Rich Tea biscuits	Grilled salmon New potatoes Peas Broccoli Fresh fruit salad Tea with skimmed milk
Wednesday	Porridge made with skimmed milk and seeds Tea with skimmed milk	One chocolate digestive biscuit Coffee with skimmed milk	Chicken breast Salad New potatoes Low-fat dressing One orange	Banana Tea with skimmed milk	Pork chop, fat removed Couscous Roasted Mediterranean vegetables Frozen yoghurt
Thursday	Bowl of cornflakes with skimmed milk One slice of wholemeal bread with low-fat spread and marmalade Tea with skimmed milk	Low fat yoghurt Coffee with skimmed milk	Tinned sardines on two slices of wholemeal toast Apple	Apple Orange juice	Vegetable lasagne Salad with low-fat salad dressing Low-fat chocolate mousse
Friday	Grilled tomatoes Two slices of wholemeal toast Orange juice Tea with skimmed milk	Cereal bar Coffee with skimmed milk	Bowl of homemade vegetable soup One wholemeal roll, no spread Apple	Two water biscuits with a small portion of reduced-fat cheese Celery	Cottage pie Courgettes Green beans
Saturday	Fresh fruit salad Two toasted crumpets with low-fat spread Coffee with skimmed milk	Pear Orange juice	Smoked mackerel Salad and tomatoes with low-fat dressing Frozen yoghurt Coffee with skimmed milk	One slice of malt loaf Tea with skimmed milk	Spaghetti Bolognese Fresh strawberries with a small amount of single cream Tea with skimmed milk

Introduction

How can you make sure you treat others of all ages, cultures and abilities fairly? Health and Social Care professionals meet people who look and sound different to them, and who have completely different backgrounds to them. This unit aims to help you understand and value the ways in which we are different so that you can better understand the diverse needs of service users in health and social care. You will learn what is meant by diversity and that it is important that all individuals have equal access to health and social care services to meet their diverse needs.

You will learn to recognise discriminatory and non-discriminatory practice in health and social care and their impact on both service users and those who work in the health and social care sector. You will then understand the importance of non-discriminatory practice in health and social care.

You will learn how health and social care practices can promote equality and diversity, looking at ways of adapting services to meet individuals' diverse needs and the benefits to service users of doing so.

The understanding you will gain can be used to help promote equality of opportunity for service users in health and social care environments. This unit covers the roles and responsibilities of service providers to promote diversity. You will also learn about legislation, codes of practice and charters that support this work.

Assessment: You will be assessed by a series of assignments set by your teacher/tutor.

Learning aims

In this unit you will:

A understand the importance of non-discriminatory practice in health and social care

B explore how health and social care practices can promote equality and diversity.

> When I went on placement to a dentist, I understood that when an older person called me 'love', he wasn't being sexist but was just speaking as all older people do in this part of the country, rather than asking my name and forgetting it.
>
> Sara, *18-year-old would-be dental nurse*

Equality and Diversity in Health and Social Care

7

BTEC
Assessment Zone

This table shows you what you must do in order to achieve a **Pass**, **Merit** or **Distinction** grade, and where you can find activities in this book to help you.

Assessment criteria			
Level 1	**Level 2 Pass**	**Level 2 Merit**	**Level 2 Distinction**
Learning aim A: Understand the importance of non-discriminatory practice in health and social care			
1A.1 Define non-discriminatory practice in health and social care, using two examples.	**2A.P1** Describe non-discriminatory and discriminatory practice in health and social care, using examples. **Assessment activity 7.1** **See page 168.**	**2A.M1** Explain the importance of legislation and codes of practice in promoting non-discriminatory practice in health and social care, using examples. **Assessment activity 7.1** **See page 168.**	**2A.D1** Assess the impact of discriminatory practice for health and social care workers, with reference to selected examples. **Assessment activity 7.1** **See page 168.**
1A.2 Identify how one code of practice or piece of legislation promotes non-discriminatory practice in health and social care.	**2A.P2** Describe how codes of practice and legislation promote non-discriminatory practice in health and social care. **Assessment activity 7.1** **See page 168.**		
Learning aim B: Explore how health and social care practices can promote equality and diversity			
1B.3 Identify the different needs of individuals in relation to health and social care provision.	**2B.P3** Describe the different needs of service users in health and social care, with reference to examples. **Assessment activity 7.2** **See page 181.**		
1B.4 Identify ways that health and social care provision can be adapted to meet the diverse needs of a selected individual.	**2B.P4** Describe how health and social care provision can be adapted to meet the diverse needs of different individuals, with reference to examples. **Assessment activity 7.2** **See page 181.**	**2B.M2** Explain the benefits of adapting health and social care provision to meet the diverse needs of different individuals, with reference to two selected examples. **Assessment activity 7.2** **See page 181.**	**2B.D2** Assess the effectiveness of health and social care provision for different individuals with diverse needs, with reference to two selected examples. **Assessment activity 7.2** **See page 181.**

How you will be assessed

The unit will be assessed by a series of internally assessed tasks. You will be expected to show an understanding of diversity in the context of health and social care sectors. The tasks will be based on a scenario in which you are working in a local health or social care organisation. For example, you may be asked to produce materials for an induction programme for new care assistants at a residential care home for older people. The care home has a wide catchment area and many of the residents come from diverse backgrounds. The manager asks you to produce training materials that can be used during the work experience induction session.

Your assessment could be in the form of:

- an induction pack or handbook; training materials such as a presentation or display; a written report, based on a case study; and/or a DVD based in a health and social care setting, such as a care home, which will:
  - identify and describe non-discriminatory and discriminatory practice for the health and social care workers
  - describe how codes of practice and current and relevant legislation promote non-discriminatory practice

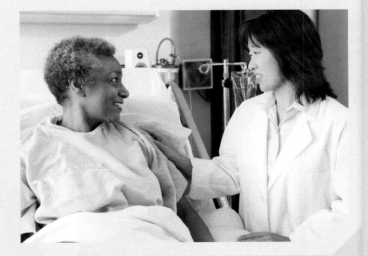

  - assess the potential impact of discriminatory practice for health and social care workers
  - identify and describe the diverse needs of two of the residents and how the home can adapt provision to meet these needs
  - identify and assess the benefits of the proposed changes in meeting their diverse needs.

A diverse society

Introduction

What do you believe in? Without sharing or discussing your ideas with your friends, write down five things you believe in. Then compare your list with others in a small group. Are you surprised at how many different things you have listed?

Link

This unit links to Units 2, 3, 4 and 8, as understanding diversity is an essential part of working with other service users and providers.

Key terms

Diversity – variety.

Culture – the beliefs, language, styles of dress, ways of cooking, religion, ways of behaving, etc. shared by a particular group of people.

Beliefs – strongly held opinions.

Discrimination – treating a person or group differently from others.

Prejudice – an unreasonable feeling against a person or group of people.

Diversity

Diversity means a variety or range of differences. To value diversity is to respect and value the **cultures** and **beliefs** of other people. If we are unwilling to accept that other people's cultures and beliefs may be different from ours, and so dismiss and ignore them, we will not be able to learn about them and understand them. Similarly, we must respect and value differences such as age, gender and disability. These factors are covered later in this unit.

A good service provider will get to know the people they work with and not make any assumptions about them. They will be open to other people's life experiences and differences, and value their diversity. They will form good relationships with their colleagues and the people who use services. A team of service providers who have different interests and skills is more likely to be able to handle the range of tasks when helping an individual, and the team will enjoy working together.

It is important to listen to and respect the beliefs of both colleagues and service users.

Non-discriminatory practice

An important aspect of health and social care work is promoting non-discriminatory practice. This means:

- not treating individuals or groups less fairly than others
- valuing diversity
- adapting care to meet diverse needs.

To really understand what non-discriminatory practice is, you need to understand **discrimination**.

Discrimination

Discrimination happens when someone has a **prejudice** against a person or a group of people. This might be for reasons such as age, gender, race, ethnicity, social class, religious beliefs, secular beliefs, family structure, sexuality, ability, health, disability, address, dress or appearance. They might then discriminate against that person or group and treat them differently.

There are four types of discrimination:

- Unfair discrimination is when a person is treated unfairly compared with someone else: for example, when someone is not considered for a job because they are older than another candidate, despite having the same qualifications and experience.
- Direct discrimination is when someone is rude, hostile or offensive to someone because they see them as being different: for example, when someone who is overweight is called names. This form of discrimination is easy to prove because it is heard or witnessed by other people.
- Indirect discrimination is harder to prove: for example, a manager may appear to be supportive and friendly towards a member of staff, but may show disrespect for their ideas by dismissing them in a jokey way.
- Positive discrimination is when a decision is made in a person's favour because there is something different about them: for example, when an advertising agency advertises for a person who has red hair and fair skin because they are to play the part of the sister of someone who has these characteristics; or when a service has few people from an ethnic minority at a certain level, so they appoint someone from an ethnic minority despite interviewing a cross-section of people.

Discriminatory and non-discriminatory practice in health and social care

Getting started ▶▶

In a small group, discuss the care which is appropriate for a person who (i) is partially sighted and has an ear infection, (ii) has mobility problems but needs to visit his dentist who has an upstairs surgery in a large dental practice with no lift.

In a whole class discussion, identify the issues with these two service users.

▼ Discriminatory practice

Stereotyping and labelling

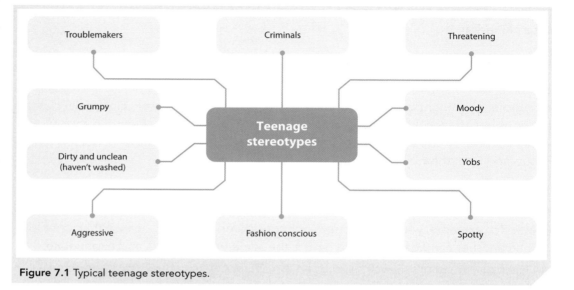

Figure 7.1 Typical teenage stereotypes.

Key terms

Judgemental – making decisions or forming opinions on the basis of something such as appearance, without proper evidence, and being too critical.

Adaptation – changing something, such as a service or device, so that it becomes suitable for a new situation or person.

Equality – equal treatment and respect.

A **stereotype** is a fixed idea about an individual or group of people: for example, someone may talk to an older person slowly, loudly and patronisingly because they assume they are deaf and intellectually less able. Other examples are shown in Figure 7.1.

When groups of people are labelled as though they are all the same, they lose their identity and assumptions are made about them; people can be very **judgemental**. Some may even decide to behave as expected, feeling that they are not valued.

Refusal of medical treatment

Refusing an individual medical treatment when another individual is given the same treatment is an example of discrimination. Examples include:

- denying a person surgery for reasons such as being morbidly obese, taking drugs or smoking
- denying a person lifesaving drugs which are very expensive but which a person living in a different area is allowed to have.

Offering inappropriate treatment or care

This may happen when a service is very busy and resources are stretched to the limit, when a health or social care professional is not being as careful as they should be, or when someone makes an assumption about a person who is behaving in a certain way. For example, when a person appears to be drunk, those around at the time may treat them with disgust and ignore them, so they are left to sleep it off, but in fact they may have suffered a stroke. By the time it is realised the person has had a stroke, it is too late for them to make a full recovery.

Giving less time than needed

If a service provider doesn't like a person they are caring for or is too busy they may not give that person as much time as is needed. For example, a person in a care home recovering from a hip replacement operation needs to keep the hip mobile by walking each day. If a carer does not make time to take the person for a walk, the hip will seize up and never give the degree of mobility it would have done if the person had been given the time to help them exercise.

Non-discriminatory practice

Providing appropriate health and social care to meet the needs of individuals

Individuals have varying needs and they must be given the appropriate health and social care to meet those needs.

Adaptations to meet diverse needs

Services can be **adapted** to meet individuals' specific needs, allowing them to maintain as much independence as possible. Some of the ways they are adapted are shown in Figure 7.2.

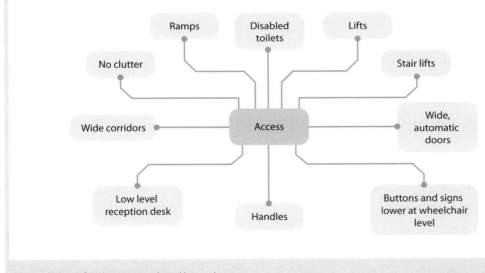

Figure 7.2a Adaptions to services (Access)

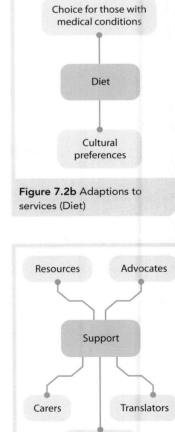

Figure 7.2b Adaptions to services (Diet)

Figure 7.2c Adaptions to services (Support)

Providing equality of access to health and social care services

Providing **equality** of access means that all individuals have the right to access the same high quality of health and social care, and service providers have the responsibility to provide this. For example, a person who is in prison is just as entitled to access health and social care as those who aren't in prison. This means that prisons have to provide their own high-quality facilities or arrange transport to use facilities outside.

Impact of discriminatory and non-discriminatory practice

Introduction

There are many effects of discrimination on service users, which you will learn about in this topic. You will then go on to learn about how non-discriminatory practice meets the diverse needs of individuals and what the law says.

Effects of discrimination on service users

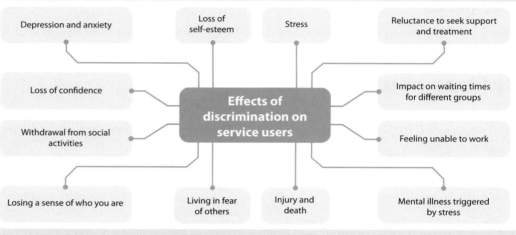

Figure 7.3 Can you think of other effects of discrimination on service users?

Did you know ?

Someone with a speech impediment, for example, may need an extra service such as an advocate (someone who speaks on their behalf) in order to access the healthcare they need.

Discussion point

What would happen in a school or college if there were no rules? Would you *really* like it? In pairs, write a list of rules you would have if you were headteacher or principal. Think about what would happen if you had your rules. Then discuss what would happen if we did not have rules, such as which side of the road we should drive on, or for sports such as football.

Non-discriminatory practice meeting the diverse needs of individuals

Everyone should receive a service of equal quality which meets their personal needs. This is not the same as everyone receiving the same service. For example, everyone should be able to register with a doctor but a more seriously ill person will require more of the doctor's time.

Treating people as individuals by taking into account their different beliefs and abilities is crucial when caring for others, and service users should acknowledge an individual's personal beliefs even if they do not share them. For example, a Muslim in hospital must be allowed to pray at certain times as this will make them feel that their identity is valued and will also help their recovery.

Meeting legal and workplace requirements

Workplaces need rules, and they come in various forms, which make sure that legal and workplace requirements are met.

- Legislation: Certain types of rules or customs may become law, and legislation (a set of laws) is introduced and passed by Parliament to make sure they are followed. One example is the law that says we drive on the left-hand side of the road in the UK. If laws are broken, the person or service breaking them can be charged with committing a crime.

- Non-discriminatory practice is a crucial part of meeting legal and workplace requirements, and includes adhering to current and relevant legislation, for example the Equality Act (2010). Equal opportunity is an approach which provides an environment in which people are not excluded from the activities of society, such as education, employment, or health and social care, on the basis of things they cannot change.

- Regulation means controlling human or society's behaviour by rules or restrictions. Regulation can be considered to be restrictions which lead to some sort of sanction or punishment, such as a fine, if they are broken.

- A charter is set out by the government and informs service users of their rights and what they can expect from **statutory** services. Many health centres and other organisations, e.g. the NHS, have charters to give service users information, such as how to access services.

Key terms

Statutory – set up and regulated by the government (according to statute or law).

Activity   Promoting non-discriminatory practice

1 Research the following legislation: Human Rights Act 1998; Equality Act 2010; Mental Health Act 2007, and Disability Discrimination Act 2005.

2 Draw up a table, showing the title of the piece of legislation in the left-hand column, and bullet points in the second column listing the importance of each Act for people who provide a health or social care service.

3 In a group, discuss why it is important in a health and social care environment for workers to understand these key pieces of legislation and how they affect their care of service users.

4 Discuss how providing halal food and a multi-faith prayer room for a Muslim hospital patient will help their recovery and promote non-discriminatory practice.

Case study

Sunshine Holidays arranges short breaks for young carers. Ben is 14 and the main carer for his mother who has MS, a condition that often reduces her ability to move around. Ben was offered a place on a two-day trip to London. Although Ben very much wanted to go on the trip, he and his mother were concerned that he would not be able to access kosher food, as the family is Jewish and follow the dietary laws strictly.

Katya, the trip organiser met with Ben and his mother and discussed how to accommodate Ben's needs on the trip. To keep the costs of the trip down, Katya was planning for the group to stay at a youth hostel with kitchen facilities, so they arranged for Ben to take some kosher ready meals. Katya also helped Ben and his mother use the internet to find a kosher take-away near to the youth hostel where he could buy a sandwich to eat for his lunch on the way home.

1 How do you think Ben felt about going on the trip before he met with Katya?

2 Identify what non-discriminatory behaviour Katya displayed.

3 Look at your notes on the Equality Act. How should this help people like Ben?

Following workplace and national codes of practice (1)

Introduction

Health and social care workers must protect service users and each other against discriminatory practice through their behaviour, attitudes and work. Non-discriminatory practice is the responsibility of both individual carers and the institution they work in. They are therefore provided with guidelines, which come in several forms. This topic looks at these and the bodies set up to enforce them.

Codes of practice

All **professional bodies** and services should have a code of practice (or code of conduct), which gives guidelines to people who work in that body or service. Any code of practice advises service providers on how to behave and standards of practice, not only to promote the individual rights of the service users, but also to protect themselves. There are many workplace and national codes of practice on different issues including non-discriminatory practice,

Regulatory bodies

These are bodies set up to make sure that the rights and responsibilities of all service users and providers are upheld, for example the Health and Care Professions Council (HCPC) regulates social workers in England. There are similar bodies that exist for the rest of the UK. They provide codes of conduct or standards of conduct, performance and ethics for social care workers and employers in a wide variety of formats.

The Health Care Professions Council's 'Standards of Conduct, Performance and Ethics' states that a social care worker must act in the best interests of service users.

You must not allow your views about a service user's sex, age, colour, race, disability, sexuality, social or economic status, lifestyle, culture, religion or beliefs to affect the way you deal with them or the professional advice you give. You must treat service users with respect and dignity.

In addition, social care workers must behave with honesty and integrity and make sure that their behaviour does not damage the public's confidence in them or their profession.

Key terms

Professional bodies – organisations that set standards for, and look after the interests of, their members, e.g. the Royal College of Nursing.

Litigation – the act or process of bringing or contesting a legal action in court.

Deregistration – to be removed from a register, e.g. no longer allowed to run a residential care home.

Safeguarding – a precautionary measure to prevent injury or abuse.

How legislation and codes of practice support non-discriminatory practice

Guidelines in their various forms, such as legislation and codes of practice, support non-discriminatory practice in health and social care by:

- protecting the carer and service user: both know the quality of care which is expected and how it will be provided. They can also be used as a basis for measuring quality of care, so provided the quality is good enough, both can be protected against unfair claims

- enforcing non-discriminatory practices and employer and employee responsibilities: both the employer and employee know their responsibilities as the guidelines make it clear what is expected of both of them

- helping avoid **litigation** and **deregistration**: carers want to avoid being sued or their institutions having their licence removed because for example, they are not providing the required quality of care. The guidelines can be used as a basis for measuring the quality of care provided.

- **safeguarding**: by having clear guidelines which support non-discriminatory practice, both carers and service users are safeguarded against possible injury or abuse. For example, safeguarding policies in schools and colleges protect children and young people under the age of 18 and provide guidance for all staff who may have any concerns of this nature.

Activity — The Nursing and Midwifery Council (NMC)

1 Look at the Code of Practice for Nursing and Social Work (May 2008) on the NMC website. In a group, discuss the ways in which it promotes non-discriminatory practice. How does it affect admission to hospital and access to advocates?

2 Imagine you are part of a group setting up a new hospital. Look at the table you drew up about key pieces of legislation and the NMC code of practice. How would these affect your plans for the new hospital? What would you need to do to make sure you follow these laws and this code of practice?

3 Think about the fact that these are just a few laws and one code of conduct; there are many more which would have to be considered if you were really setting up a new service. In your group, discuss what some of these might be.

Following workplace and national codes of practice (2)

Here are some questions to test what you have learned. You can then complete a practice assessment assignment.

Just checking

1 What is meant by diversity and why is it important to value it?
2 Name the four types of discrimination.
3 Is it ever right to use discrimination in the health and social care workplace? Explain your answer.
4 What is meant by being (i) judgemental, and (ii) stereotypical?
5 Give three examples of non-discriminatory practice in health and social care.
6 Give five possible effects of discrimination on a health and social care service user.
7 What is equality of opportunity?
8 What do we mean by legislation?
9 What is a charter? Give an example.
10 Why is it important to follow workplace and national codes of practice?
11 Explain three ways in which legislation and codes of practice support non-discriminatory practice in health and social care.

Assessment activity 7.1 | English | 2A.P1 | 2A.P2 | 2A.M1 | 2A.D1

You are a trainee care assistant at a residential care home for older people on the outskirts of a small city. You have been asked to write a chapter of an induction handbook for new staff which describes non-discriminatory and discriminatory practice, how codes of practice and current and relevant legislation promote non-discriminatory practice, and assesses the potential impact of discriminatory practice for health and social care workers in the care home.

You should examine at least two codes of practice from two different local care homes and compare and describe the ways they support non-discriminatory practice and promote the diverse needs of service users.

Your chapter should include the use of at least two examples to explain the importance of non-discriminatory practice and to assess the impact of discriminatory practice for health and social care workers.

Tips

When describing discriminatory and non-discriminatory practices, you should mention at least three types of practice, as listed earlier in this unit.

WorkSpace

▼ SALEEM SINGH

Care Assistant

I am a care assistant in a busy residential care home for older people. I work in a team which includes many other care assistants, nursing staff, a manager, a matron, a chef, domestic workers who change beds and take food and drink to residents, and cleaners. We have ninety separate rooms, so residents can have their own room although a few rooms have married couples in them. There are also two TV lounges and two dining rooms, so residents who choose to can mix together for certain activities, as well as a staffroom where staff can keep their personal belongings and offices for the manger and matron.

My main task is to look after the residents in a number of rooms which are all in the same area of the home. I help them wash and dress each morning, get them settled either in their rooms or in the TV lounge, and do whatever else needs doing during the day. This includes taking their food orders, accompanying them to the dining room, keeping them company if they are feeling lonely or sad and want a chat, taking them to the toilet if they are unsteady on their feet, and arranging any visiting services for them, such as the hairdresser or chiropodist. I enjoy helping them to maintain as much independence as possible and making their lives easier and happier. It is lovely to meet their families too, although it can be very sad sometimes, such as when a resident is taken ill, has a fall, or dies, but I then try to make things as easy as possible for the family.

I love my job because I work with a wide range of people who are mostly very nice and who have a lot of experience of life and many stories to tell. I feel that I am making a real difference to them.

Think about it

1 Why is it so important for Saleem to understand the diverse needs of the residents of the care home?

2 Do you feel that you understand how diverse the needs of our multicultural society are? Does the area you live in reflect this diversity? If not, what do you think you can do to increase your understanding?

3 Do you think you carry out non-discriminatory practice in your everyday life? If not, how will you improve this?

Factors that may affect care needs (1)

Introduction

There are a range of factors which may affect the diverse needs of service users in health and social care. You will usually need to consider many factors at the same time. In this topic you will learn about three of these: gender, sexual orientation and gender reassignment.

Gender

Traditionally women were expected to stay at home and look after the house and family. As the years have passed, changes have occurred that have made men and women more equal, including legislation that makes it illegal to discriminate against someone because of their gender.

All individuals should have their personal preferences acknowledged and catered for where possible. Both genders should have the option of being treated in single-sex wards; patients often feel that being on a mixed-sex ward can reduce their privacy and dignity at a time when they are already feeling **vulnerable**. Some patients are opposed to mixed-sex accommodation for cultural or religious reasons. However, it is necessary to have mixed-sex accommodation when patients need urgent or highly specialised care.

Some people prefer to receive medical treatment and personal care from health and social care workers of their own gender, for example having a female doctor doing a smear test, while others have religious reasons for this.

Key terms

Vulnerable – open to being hurt emotionally or physically.

Remember

When working in health and social care, you need to ensure that you have a person's permission to share information about their sexuality. For example, a patient in hospital may not wish their parents to be given any information that would suggest that the patient is gay. This would include avoiding references to the patient being visited by their partner. Social care workers need to show respect for the sexual orientation of both carers and service users. Workers are also entitled to work without suffering discrimination for their own sexual orientation by either their employer or by people using their service.

Activity   Rights of women

1 Carry out some research to show how the rights of women have changed since the start of the nineteenth century. Draw a timeline to show key events.

2 Think about jobs in the health and social care sector. When you go to your local hospital, are the nurses and doctors mainly men or women? What about your dentist, GP and optician? Think about other jobs in this sector. Compare your thoughts with those of the rest of your group.

3 Discuss whether you think there are some jobs in health and social care that are better done by women than men, and vice versa. Explain why you think this.

Sexual orientation

A person's sexual orientation refers to the gender to which he or she is sexually attracted. Most people are heterosexual (attracted to the opposite sex), some are homosexual (attracted to the same sex) and some are bisexual (attracted to both sexes).

The Civil Partnership Act 2004 allowed homosexual people to have a legal partnership that gives them the same rights as married partners. Some people struggle with their homosexual feelings, sometimes hiding them for years and even marrying someone of the opposite sex, but this affects their health and wellbeing and care needs.

Case study

Aurel is homosexual, but has hidden his true feelings all his life. He is 45 years old, has a wife, two children and a high-profile job as a surgeon. Lately he has become more and more unsettled and has met a man in a gay bar he feels he could be happy with. He is afraid to tell his wife because he does not want to break the family up. He is worried that he will lose his children's love and his parents' respect, and that his colleagues and patients will be unhappy working with and being treated by a gay man.

1   In a group, discuss Aurel's predicament. (i) What do you think he should do? (ii) What do you think the effects will be on his health and wellbeing if he doesn't admit his true feelings? (iii) What do you think the effects will be on his health and wellbeing if he admits his true feelings?

2   Role-play the situation when he tells his wife and family, and then his work colleagues (i) where they are supportive, and (ii) where they are unsupportive.

Gender reassignment

Some people are born feeling very unhappy about their gender, and eventually go through gender reassignment therapy to become a member of the opposite gender. This consists of hormone replacement therapy to change secondary sexual characteristics, such as facial hair, and gender reassignment surgery to alter primary sexual characteristics, such as the sex organs and permanent hair removal for women.

Many people hide their desire for gender reassignment for many years, which is why some undergo therapy to cope with the mental health issues of anxiety, stress and various addictions. Service users and carers have the right to have their choice of gender respected and to be addressed in the correct way.

Activity   Gender reassignment

1   If you wanted to be the opposite gender, how do you think it would make (i) you, (ii) your family, and (iii) your friends feel?

2   Do some research into people in the public eye who either dress as though they are of the opposite gender, or who have undergone full gender reassignment. How has it affected their lives? What have been their health and social care needs, and how were they met?

Factors that may affect care needs (2)

Introduction

In this topic, you will learn about more factors that may affect the care needs of individuals: age, disability, marriage and civil partnership, pregnancy and maternity, and race.

Age

Two hundred years ago, if you lived beyond the age of 50, you were considered to be old and to have lived a long life.

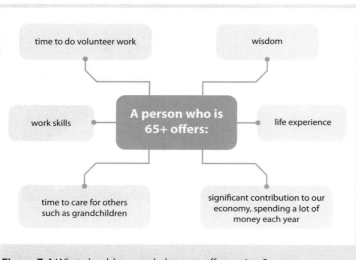

Figure 7.4 What do older people have to offer society?

Diagram text:
- time to do volunteer work
- wisdom
- work skills
- **A person who is 65+ offers:**
- life experience
- time to care for others such as grandchildren
- significant contribution to our economy, spending a lot of money each year

More people are living longer nowadays because of advances in medical science and greater health awareness, so the population of the UK is increasing, with a greater number of older people in our society than ever before. Our society contains many active and healthy older people, as well as many who are less active and healthy and in residential care of some kind. This affects health and social care services.

The appropriate formal form of address and language should be used by carers of older people as they often do not like being called by their first name, feeling it is too informal and lacks respect. This can cause resentment and affect the service user's recovery or rehabilitation as they may not engage with the help being offered as readily.

Activity   Older people

1 In a small group, discuss the implications of people living longer on (i) society in general, (ii) their families, (iii) health services, and (iv) social care services.

2 Cut pictures out of magazines or print them off the internet of people over the age of 65. Divide them into positive images and negative images, and produce two separate collages.

3 As a class, discuss young people's attitudes towards older people. Look at Figure 7.4. If you don't know the meaning of 'wisdom' and 'life experience', your teacher/tutor will explain them to you.

Disability

Whatever condition a person has, their needs include all those of an able-bodied person, but they have important additional needs, especially in relation to accessing places and services. A disability may affect physical fitness, restrict access to learning activities, cause emotional distress and remove some social opportunities, thus affecting health and wellbeing. It may also affect the growth and physical development of the body and the development of new abilities and skills, as well as emotional development. It is therefore essential that a disabled person has equality of access to health and social care services.

Marriage and civil partnership

Many people choose to commit to their partner through marriage or a civil partnership, but others choose to just live together. Carers must show respect for the service user's choice regarding involvement of their partners or family in their care. Health and social care services may need to be adapted to provide accommodation for married couples to live together.

Pregnancy and maternity

A pregnant service user has a right to choose a birth plan, usually on the understanding that if things go wrong, the safest options for the mother and baby will be taken. The birth plan includes wishes such as having the baby at home or in hospital; pain relief or a natural birth; use of a birthing pool; choice of birthing partner, and the form of post-natal care (breastfeeding or not).

Race

The term 'race' is used to describe a person's genetic heritage, meaning **traits** that are socially significant, such as skin colour. **Ethnicity** refers to a person's cultural background.

Regardless of appearance, ethnic or national origin, everyone has an equal right to access health and social care services. Depending on their cultural background, people often have different expectations of how they wish to be addressed, or how they should interact with others. For people to be able to access health and social care services fully, their ethnic and national identity must be considered. Giving people appropriate choices about their lives and the treatment they receive maintains their dignity and improves the quality of the care they receive.

Key terms

Trait – a particular quality in someone's character.

Ethnicity – being part of a group sharing the same way of life and culture.

Case study

Mary is from the traveller community. Her two-year-old son, Damon, has been ill recently and had to spend some time in hospital. At the first follow-up appointment with the GP, Mary and Damon were accompanied by several members of their extended family, and the GP refused to allow them all into his room. However, after speaking to Mary, he learned that within the traveller community, family members expect to be included in discussions and decisions about health. He arranged for the extended family to wait outside while he examined Damon, and then to come back into his room for the discussion about his progress. When Damon is well again, the family plans to travel around the country for several months over the summer.

1 How did the GP adapt the health and social care service to Mary's needs?

2 What are the benefits to Mary and her family of the GP's actions?

3 When Mary's family starts to travel again, how might this affect their ability to access health and social care services?

4 Research how your local council helps travellers overcome these problems.

Factors that may affect care needs (3)

Introduction

The final factors affecting the care needs of individuals which you will learn about in this topic are religion and belief, social class, family structure and geographical location.

Key terms

Religion – a set of beliefs based on the idea of a sacred being.

Secular – something that has no connection to any religion or place of worship.

Social class – a group of people who share a common place in society.

Cohabiting – people living together in an emotionally and/ or sexually intimate relationship.

Religion and belief

A **religion** is a set of beliefs which is based on the idea of a sacred being, or god. **Secular** beliefs, however, have no connection to religion or a place of worship: for example, the beliefs of a political party. Individuals have different needs relating to their beliefs and practices. You will learn more about these needs later in this unit.

Social class

Social class is to do with the status that an individual has in society. This is based mainly on occupation, wealth and lifestyle. The higher up a class system a person belongs, the more power, influence and wealth they tend to have. All service users and carers should have a right to equality of access to health and social care services regardless of their social class.

Activity   Family tree

Draw a quick family tree for your family. How does it differ, if at all, from the others in your class?

Link

This topic links to Unit 4: Social Influences on Health and Wellbeing.

Family structure

A family is a social group made up of people who are related to each other by birth, marriage or adoption. Being part of a family shows others that those people are connected in some way. We can classify four different types of family:

- The extended family: this consists of three or even four generations of one family who live together (or near each other) and have very regular contact with each other. This type of family is becoming less common in our society, but remains important in countries such as Italy. The advantages of such a family are a strong support network for help when, for example, parents work or someone is sick. They also support each other financially and help the development of children. Health and social care services may need to be adapted to allow greater participation in care, and care planning, by family members.

- The nuclear family: this includes two parents (who may be married or **cohabiting**) and their children. This is a more common family structure than the extended family in the UK. Health and social care services may need to be adapted to take into account the working patterns of both parents.

- The single-parent family: this family has one parent, maybe because of divorce, separation, being widowed or never having had a relationship with the other parent. It is more usual for the children to live with the mother. These families are more likely to struggle financially. Health and social services may need to be adapted to take into account financial need, and that it may be difficult for a single parent to arrange childcare to attend appointments.

- The reconstituted family: in this type of family, an individual with children develops a relationship with another person who may or may not have children from a previous relationship. They may go on to have children together. The family therefore has at least one step-parent. Health and social care services may need to be adapted to take into account that children from reconstituted families often spend time in different locations, and may not always have easy access to their registered services.

Activity	Families

Draw up a table listing the advantages and disadvantages of living in (i) a nuclear family, (ii) a reconstituted family, and (iii) no family, and compare the three. Remember to include the impact on care needs.

Geographical location

Where people live affects their needs and their access to health and social care. Someone living in a rural area will have the benefit of less air, light and noise pollution, and the countryside to walk in, but may have to travel further to access a service. In a built-up area, there may be too many people trying to access a service, so longer waiting lists.

Access to health care can be difficult in rural locations.

Religion and belief (1)

Introduction

One of the main differences in our society and across the world is in the beliefs we hold. There is a wide range of religious or secular beliefs. For people working in health and social care, it is important to have an understanding about the beliefs of those you come into contact with. Some religious and secular beliefs directly affect care needs, but it can also be useful to know some background information about what people consider to be important. This topic looks at Christianity and Islam.

Activity   Places of worship

All hospitals, hospices and many other health and social care settings provide a multi-denominational room where people can worship or simply sit and reflect. In a small group, discuss why this is necessary and what the benefits are.

► Christianity

- **Beliefs:** Christians believe in God. Christianity began in the Middle East over 2,000 years ago from the teachings of Jesus Christ. Christians believe that Jesus Christ lived a humble and selfless life, died to save humanity by taking our sins with him, and rose from the dead. God is the Trinity of the Father, Son (Jesus) and Holy Spirit. Christians believe that when they die, they will join God in the kingdom of heaven for **eternity**. They follow the Ten Commandments, which they believe were given to Moses by God.

- **Festivals and holy days:** The main Christian day is Sunday, which has traditionally been seen as a day of rest. Christians celebrate many festivals, including Christmas when they celebrate Jesus' birth, and Easter, the death and resurrection of Jesus.

- **Food and diet:** Some Christians fast or give up a food they enjoy for the 40 days of Lent, which come before Easter. Otherwise there is no special Christian diet.

- **Forms of worship:** People are baptised, usually as babies, by having a cross drawn with water on their forehead to welcome them into the Christian faith. Christians worship on a Sunday by going to church and taking part in a variety of services, at which they sing hymns of praise and pray to God. One of these services is Holy Communion, where those who have been confirmed eat a wafer of bread to represent Christ's body and drink communion wine to represent his blood.

- **Dress:** There is no Christian form of dress except for the church ministers, some of whom wear long robes to lead services.

- **Symbols:** The main symbol of the Christian faith is the cross on which Jesus was crucified. The holy book is the Bible, consisting of the Old Testament (shared with the Jewish faith) and the New Testament, which tells the story of Jesus' birth, life, death and resurrection, and contains his teachings.

- **Health and medical beliefs:** some Christian groups are opposed to abortion and stem cell research.

Key terms

Eternity – an endless amount of time.

Islam

- Beliefs: Muslims have six main beliefs, called the Articles of Faith. They believe in:
  - Allah – the primary Muslim belief is that there is only one god, called Allah in Arabic, and that Muhammad is the messenger of Allah
  - angels
  - the holy book, which is the Qur'an
  - the prophets, or special messengers, such as Ibrahim (Abraham) and Muhammad
  - the day of judgement, when the life of every human being will be assessed to decide whether they go to heaven or hell
  - predestination, that Allah has already decided what will happen in the world, although this does not stop humans making free choices.

- Festivals and holy days: There are two main holy days in Islam, Eid ul Fitr, which occurs at the end of the holy fasting month of Ramadan, and Eid ul Adha, which commemorates Ibrahim's obedience to God in agreeing to sacrifice his son.

- Food and diet: the only meat Muslims will eat is halal meat that has been killed according to religious practice. Eating pork is forbidden. For the holy month of Ramadan, religious Muslims do not eat during daylight hours.

- Forms of worship: Muslims pray up to five times each day and some attend the mosque for these prayers. They use prayer mats and they must face Mecca, wherever they are in the world. Religious practices include the Five Pillars of Islam, which are five duties that unite Muslims into a community.

- Dress: Both men and women are required to dress modestly. Some Muslim women wear a headscarf to cover their hair and neck, and a few choose to cover their faces as well.

- Symbols: There are no official symbols in Islam, but the crescent and star are often associated with the religion.

- Health and medical beliefs: Muslim boys are usually circumcised, which may have some health benefits. Among many possible adaptations, health and social care services may need to be adapted to take into account a Muslim's wish to pray, to eat halal food and to fast during Ramadan. Muslims may wish to receive treatment in a single-sex ward and personal care from someone of their own sex.

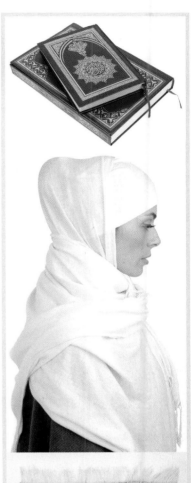

Can you identify these items?

Activity   Hinduism

1. Carry out research on Hinduism. Include details about (i) food, (ii) dress, (iii) symbols, (iv) health and medical beliefs, and (v) festivals and holy days. Use the information to produce an information leaflet with pictures.

2. In a small group, discuss how hospital staff would have to adapt their care to meet the needs of (i) a Muslim, and (ii) a Hindu patient.

3. Discuss how such adaptations would help the patient's recovery. Share your ideas in a group discussion. Visit Pearson hotlinks to view websites that will be very useful for this activity.

Religion and belief (2)

Introduction

In this topic you will learn about Judaism and Buddhism, which some consider to be a religion and others a secular group. People who work in health and social care may find it useful to know details about the beliefs of service users in order to be able to adapt care where necessary.

Key terms

Atonement – something done to make up for an injury or wrong.

Kosher – food that satisfies the requirements of Jewish law; for example, when an animal is slaughtered, all the blood must be drained from its body before it can be eaten.

Circumcision – male circumcision is the removal of some or all of the foreskin from the penis.

Judaism

- Beliefs: Judaism began in the Middle East over 3,500 years ago. Jews believe that God created the world and everything in it, and that God appointed the Jews to be his chosen people in order to set an example of holiness and ethical behaviour to the world. They follow the Ten Commandments. Judaism was founded by Moses. The Jewish holy book is known as the Tanakh.

- Festivals and holy days: Judaism has a number of festivals and holy days. The most important days in the Jewish calendar are Rosh Hashanah, which is the Jewish New Year, and Yom Kippur, the Day of **Atonement**. Other holy days include Pesach (Passover), which lasts for eight days and is celebrated in spring. It reminds Jews that their ancestors were once slaves in Egypt and that God helped them to flee from slavery. Shabbat (Sabbath) is the weekly holy day, which lasts from sunset on Friday evening to Saturday night.

- Food and diet: To celebrate Shabbat, Jews eat bread called challah, made in the shape of a plait, and drink wine. Jewish people buy their meat and other foods from specialist **kosher** shops and butchers. They do not eat pork, rabbit or shellfish and they have different sets of utensils, one to use with meat and one with milk, because meat and milk foods are never prepared or eaten together.

- Forms of worship: the Jewish holy book is made up of the Torah (five books of Moses), the books of the Prophets, and holy writings. Jewish people worship in the synagogue and their spiritual leaders are called Rabbis.

- Dress: Orthodox Jewish men wear tefillin (cubic black leather boxes with leather straps) on their head and their arm during weekday morning prayers. Orthodox Jewish men always cover their heads by wearing a skullcap known in Hebrew as a kippah or in Yiddish as a yarmulke.

- Symbols: The Star of David is the best-known symbol of Judaism. Another symbol is the Menorah, a seven-branched candlestick.

- Health and medical beliefs: The Brit Milah (**circumcision** ceremony) is an important initiation rite for Jewish baby boys.

Buddhism

- Beliefs: Buddhists believe that life is one long cycle (the samsar) which consists of birth, life, death and rebirth. After death, a person's soul is reborn in a new body and the only way to break the cycle is to reach enlightenment (nirvana), the end of everything that is not perfect such as greed, hatred, suffering and ignorance. The Buddha was simply a human being, called Siddhartha Gautama, who was born into royalty but left his privileged life to find enlightenment when he saw the suffering of others. Buddha means 'Awakened One'. There are various forms of Buddhism, each of which believes in different routes to reach enlightenment.

- Festivals: The most important Buddhist festival is Wesak (or Buddha Day), which is held on the first day of the full moon in May or June. On this day the Buddha is thought to have been born, gained enlightenment and passed away, all in different years.

- Food and diet: Most Buddhists are strict vegetarians because they are opposed to causing harm to any living creature.

- Forms of worship: Buddhists worship in a temple or monastery, and often meditate as well.

- Dress: Some Buddhist monks wear a red, yellow or saffron robe.

- Symbols: The wheel (Chakra) is one of the most important Buddhist symbols, as it represents the teachings of the Buddha.

What other Buddhist symbols are there?

- Health and medical beliefs: Since prayer is part of the healing and cleansing process, prayer and meditation are important to enable medications and other medical treatments to assist with healing. Some holy days include fasting from dawn to dusk, but considerations are allowed for the frail and elderly, for whom fasting could create problems. Terminal illness may be seen as a unique opportunity to reflect on life's ultimate meaning, and the meaning of one's relationship with the world. Therefore, it is important that medication does not interfere with consciousness.

? Did you know?

Richard Gere, Orlando Bloom, Harrison Ford, Keanu Reeves, Tiger Woods, Pamela Stephenson, Tina Turner and Joanna Lumley are just a few celebrities who have taken up Buddhism.

Adapting services

Getting started ▶▶

In small groups, discuss *either* how you think the world began, *or* what you think happens to a person when they die. Discuss the ways in which your opinions differ and where your ideas came from.

Introduction

Atheists and humanists have their own beliefs which should be respected in the same way as religious beliefs, as it is important to value diversity in order to promote equality of opportunity for all service users. Health and social care provision is adapted to meet the diverse needs of service users. In this topic, you will learn about adapting services.

Secular groups

Atheists

Atheists do not believe in any god. They think that God and religion are man-made myths and legends, and so are not meaningful. Atheism is not a set of beliefs, but an absence of belief in God. Health and social care services may need to be adapted for atheists. For example, in a care home that holds a Christian service on Sundays, space needs to be available for atheists so that they don't feel their beliefs are being dismissed.

Humanists

Humanism is a positive set of beliefs about people and ethics. Humanists do not believe in any god. They celebrate events such as weddings, but the ceremony is centred on the people involved rather than a religion.

Adapting services to meet needs

Service users in health and social care have diverse care needs and there are many factors that can affect these. Adaptations are made to services to meet service users' specific needs so that they can maintain as much independence as possible. You must be able to relate the adaptations to services to the factors that are covered in this unit.

In addition to the adaptations you have learned about in this unit, visiting arrangements in a hospital or care home are adapted to meet the needs of service users. Families and friends can visit at set times in the afternoon and evening. Outside of visiting times, service users are given as much rest as possible and their dignity preserved, and the staff can focus on providing the required care service.

Benefits of adapting provision

There are a range of benefits to service users of adapting health and social care provision to meet their diverse needs. If service users are happy with the provision they receive, this will aid their recovery and rehabilitation.

The benefits include:

- being respected
- being treated equally
- not being discriminated against
- maintaining dignity and privacy
- feeling safe
- receiving improved quality of care
- receiving personalised care
- improved accessibility of health and social care
- having their needs met.

Activity   Humanists

Carry out some research on humanists. Prepare a PowerPoint presentation to show how humanists make the following non-religious: (i) naming ceremonies, (ii) weddings, and (iii) funerals.

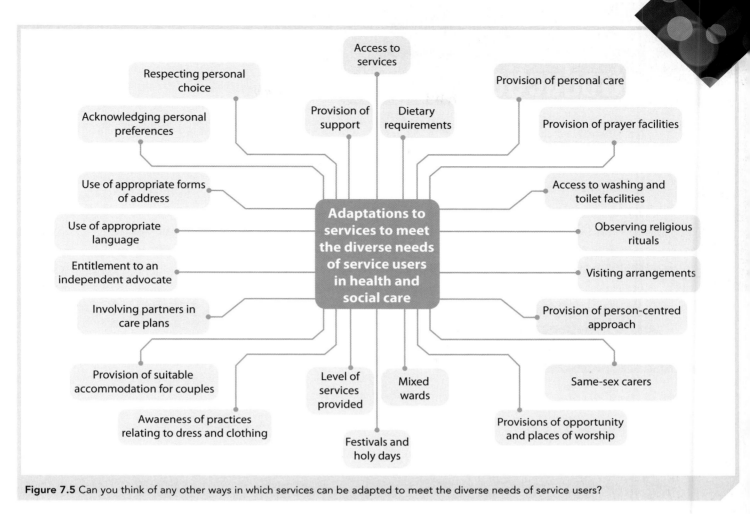

Figure 7.5 Can you think of any other ways in which services can be adapted to meet the diverse needs of service users?

Assessment activity 7.2 English 2B.P3 | 2B.P4 | 2B.M2 | 2B.D2

In your role as a trainee care assistant at a residential care home for older people on the outskirts of a small city, you are approached by two new care assistants who have read the chapter of the handbook which you wrote. They ask you how health and social care provision in the home could be adapted to meet the diverse needs of the two residents they are to care for. The manager asks you to produce a presentation for them, in which you will describe the residents' diverse needs and how provision could be adapted to meet these needs.

You must then explain how your ideas on how adapting services will benefit the service users, and assess how effective these proposed changes are likely to be in meeting their diverse needs.

Note that the residents of the care home have a wide range of health and social care needs as it is also a nursing home, and therefore accepts older people with conditions such as dementia.

Tips

You must give a clear description of the potential needs related to all the factors listed in this unit, using at least one example for each factor.

Activity Adapting services

Look at Figure 7.5. In a small group, discuss any adaptations which have not been mentioned in detail in this unit. How do you think they help meet diverse needs?

Introduction

We all know what is right and fair, don't we, so why is it so important that we have a whole unit devoted to this subject? But do we? Do you really know your 'rights'? And do we all have the same rights? Are people all treated the same, even if they do not look or act the same as others?

Health care professionals are quite likely to meet people who do not have the same ideas and behaviours as they do. This unit will help you understand why it is important to ensure all people who use health and social care services, and colleagues, are treated equally and fairly.

Assessment: You will be assessed by a series of assignments set by your teacher/tutor.

Learning aims

In this unit you will:

A investigate the rights of individuals using health and social care services

B examine the responsibilities of employers and employees in upholding service users' rights in health and social care.

> When I am at my Saturday job in the care home I always ask the residents if they want me to help them. I used to just do things for them without asking, but I now realise that I was often taking away their independence and not allowing them to make choices about what they wanted to do or wear.
>
> Martin, *16-year-old would-be social worker*

Individual Rights in Health and Social Care

8

BTEC
Assessment Zone

This table shows you what you must do in order to achieve a **Pass**, **Merit** or **Distinction** grade, and where you can find activities in this book to help you.

Assessment criteria			
Level 1	**Level 2 Pass**	**Level 2 Merit**	**Level 2 Distinction**
Learning aim A: Investigate the rights of individuals using health and social care services			
1A.1 Identify the individual rights of service users in health and social care.	**2A.P1** Summarise the individual rights of service users in health and social care. **Assessment activity 8.1 See page 194.**	**2A.M1** Explain ways in which service users' individual rights can be upheld in health and social care, using selected examples. **Assessment activity 8.1 See page 194.**	**2A.D1** Assess the benefits and potential difficulties of upholding service users' rights in health and social care, using selected examples. **Assessment activity 8.1 See page 194.**
1A.2 Identify how current and relevant legislation protects the rights of service users, with reference to one example.	**2A.P2** Describe how current and relevant legislation protects the rights of service users, using examples. **Assessment activity 8.1 See page 194.**		
Learning aim B: Examine the responsibilities of employers and employees in upholding service users' rights in health and social care			
1B.3 Identify how an employee can plan to maximise the safety of service users.	**2B.P3** Describe how an employee can plan to maximise the safety of service users. **Assessment activity 8.2 See page 201.**	**2B.M2** Explain why risk assessment is important in health and social care. **Assessment activity 8.2 See page 201.**	**2B.D2** Evaluate the importance of the use of risk assessments in health and social care, using selected examples. **Assessment activity 8.2 See page 201.**
1B.4 Identify how the right to confidentiality is protected in health and social care.	**2B.P4** Describe how the right to confidentiality is protected in health and social care. **Assessment activity 8.3 See page 205.**	**2B.M3** Explain why the right to confidentiality is protected in health and social care, using examples. **Assessment activity 8.3 See page 205.**	**2B.D3** Justify occasions where there is a need for an employee to breach confidentiality, using examples. **Assessment activity 8.3 See page 205.**

How you will be assessed

The unit will be assessed by a series of internally assessed tasks. You will be expected to show an understanding of communication skills in the context of health and social care sectors. The tasks will be based on a scenario where you work in a local health or social care organisation.

Your assessment could be in the form of:

- a written observation log based in health or social care settings
- training materials, such as leaflets, posters and PowerPoint presentations
- a training DVD demonstrating good practice through role play.

Rights of individuals using services

INK   A.1

Getting started

Everyone in society has **rights** that are protected by law. When people are using health and social care services, they are often in a vulnerable position. It is very important that everyone working in health and social care understands what rights service users have and how to uphold them.

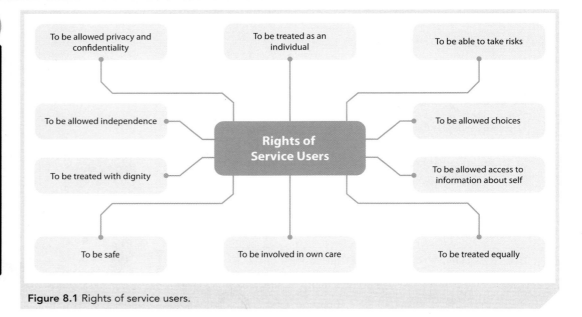

Figure 8.1 Rights of service users.

Key terms

Rights – things that a person can claim they are free to do or that are due to them.

Dignity – a calm and serious manner/style suitable for the situation and to treat someone with respect.

Self-esteem – how much you like, accept and respect yourself as a person, how you value yourself.

The spider diagram shows the **rights** of each individual using health and social care services, but what do these rights really mean?

- To be respected – we show respect to others by the way we address each other and the attitudes that we display. The way in which we listen to the views and opinions of other people and how we value privacy and confidentiality are all part of respecting each other.

- To be treated as an individual – we are each unique and expect to be treated as an individual person, not the same as everyone else. We should always treat others as individuals, trying not to generalise and not to lump people together in categories, for example, 'all teenage girls have long hair' or 'all old people have arthritis and walk with a stick'.

- Treating people with **dignity** ensures that they keep their self-respect and **self-esteem**. For example, many people – not just the elderly – can have a problem with incontinence, which means that they might not get to the toilet in time. This can make the individual feel embarrassed and ashamed. The behaviour and attitude of their care workers can help overcome these feelings and allow the individual to maintain their dignity.

- All individuals have the right to be treated equally and not discriminated against. This does not mean treating everyone the same, but behaving towards them fairly whatever their gender, social class, sexuality, age, race, ability, where they live, etc.

- Being allowed privacy means freedom from the attention or intrusion of others into an individual's private life and affairs, and that any information about them should remain confidential.

- To be allowed access to information about themselves. By ensuring that individuals have access to information held about them helps them make choices about their care and treatment. This in turn helps raise self-esteem and feelings of respect.

- By allowing individuals to have account taken of their choices (e.g. to communicate in preferred method/language) helps support their **independence** and raise their self-esteem.

- Allowing independence means that individuals are not dependent or controlled by another person or organisation.

- We all have the right to be safe and to be free from harm. All health and social care settings must have a health and safety policy that sets out rules, regulations and actions that must be followed.

- Being independent and able to make choices could mean that an individual might wish to take risks. Risks should be managed carefully to ensure that hazards are identified and eliminated or reduced.

- Being involved in their own care means that individuals feel their opinions and feelings are important and that they are respected as independent people.

Key terms

Independence – freedom from control by, or dependence on, others.

Protecting privacy: how does using a secure filing cabinet for records help to protect service users' rights?

Activity   Rights of service users

Look at Figure 8.1. Some of the rights seem to contradict some of the others.

1 With a partner, discuss an example of each of the rights.

2 Can you identify any problems in ensuring all of these rights are upheld?

3 Are some of the rights more important than others?

4 Make brief notes on your discussion so that you can present them to the rest of the group.

Upholding service users' rights (1)

Getting started

One of our rights is to have our choices taken into account.

We know how important it is that we can make our own decisions and that in order to make those decisions we need to have choices – but does everyone have that opportunity?

Consider these questions:

Did you decide what to wear today and what to eat? Did you decide whether to have a bath, a shower or just a quick wash?

How would you feel if your clothes and food were always decided for you – with no opportunity to choose something different?

Introduction

It should be the aim of all service providers to promote a way of life for service users that allows them to enjoy, as far as possible, their rights as individuals.

Through **empowerment**, individual users of a service can feel that their opinions are valued and respected. Too often individuals being cared for have their needs, wishes and expectations ignored. For example, the carer will select clothes to be worn because they are easy to put on, or food to be eaten because it is quick to prepare, not thinking that the individual might wish to choose their own clothes and food. Having choice in their lives helps people maintain their independence, dignity and positive self-image.

A person-centred approach

Taking a **person-centred approach** is one way of upholding service users' rights. By taking a person-centred approach carers ensure that the service user is the most important person. The service user should be included in planning and decision-making about their life. Their support should always be matched to their needs, not what is most efficient or practical for the care provider.

Taking part in writing their own care plan and in evaluating the care they are given can empower service users and help give feelings of **fulfilment**.

Key terms

Empowerment – enabling individuals to take responsibility for their own lives by making informed decisions.

Person-centred approach – working with individuals to identify their values, needs and expectations.

Fulfilment – the opportunity to accomplish personal goals and use abilities to the full.

Infringing – going too far, or overstepping the mark.

Case study

Thomas is 78 and lives in a care home. Recently a new care assistant has been assigned to Thomas. She visits Thomas's room at 9.30 each evening, and turns off the television and takes the remote control from the room. The care assistant then removes Thomas's hearing aid, saying that he will not need it as the television is now off.

1 How is this **infringing** Thomas's rights?

2 What choices is Thomas being given?

3 Should Thomas be given any options?

4 As a 78 year old, what time should Thomas go to bed?

5 Should Thomas be allowed to turn the television on during the night?

6 How much independence do you think Thomas feels he has?

Ensuring privacy during personal care

Just checking

1 What does 'empowerment' mean?
2 Give three examples of care that might empower a service user.

In the very recent past it was common practice for toilet doors in many care settings to not have a lock. While a lock on a toilet door is not a 'right' in itself, the lack of a lock meant that the right to privacy during personal care was not being respected. Imagine how you would feel if you could not use the toilet or bathroom in privacy.

Ensuring that a service user can use the toilet or bathroom with as much privacy as possible helps to maintain their dignity. Maintaining dignity can help to boost self-esteem and increase people's quality of life.

How do you feel if you have to use a toilet without a lock?

Activity   Promoting rights

Shona is a young adult who has severe learning disabilities and lives in a care home. She also has similar needs and expectations to any other young person.

- Give at least five examples of how you might promote Shona's rights by supporting them in controlling their own life.
- Devise a set of guidelines that could be used to promote the rights of service users in a residential home for young adults with learning disabilities.

Upholding service users' rights (2)

Introduction

Making sure that you don't discriminate against service users and that you use empathy and honesty when communicating are important parts of upholding service users' rights.

◤ Anti-discriminatory practices

Sometimes discrimination is deliberate (for example refusing to employ someone because of their gender or race), but it also happens because institutions or individuals have not thought about how their actions might affect others.

For people working in health and social care, it is very important to take an active role in ensuring that the service they provide does not discriminate against service users.

The right to be able to communicate in the method or language of choice is important for individuals being cared for, as this helps to ensure that users of services can take part in making decisions. If a service user is used to using British Sign Language (BSL) for instance, then the service provider should find someone who can communicate in BSL. The need for effective communication is of the highest importance.

Making sure that all service users have access to food that meets their dietary and religious requirements is another form of anti-discriminatory practice.

It is also important to ensure that all service users can physically access a service, for example making sure that buildings are accessible or that written information is available in large print, Braille or appropriate languages.

◤ Empathy and honesty

Care workers should try to ensure that service users are respected for being the people they are through **empathy** – not **sympathy**. In this way, a care worker can support an individual and enable the person to maintain their dignity.

Empathy is shown by the way that a care worker speaks to users of services, the words that they use and the non-verbal communication that they demonstrate.

When you sympathise with someone you feel sorry for them and have pity for their situation. Sympathy is often a negative approach and is not helpful in dealing with issues or problems.

Honesty and empathy are two major characteristics of the worker in health and social care.

When you empathise with someone, you show that you can identify with them, understand how they are feeling and put yourself in their position. However, this is not always easy if you have not experienced what the other person is feeling or the situation they are in, you might find it hard to put yourself in their position – but you can tell them this, and ask them to explain their situation and feelings to you.

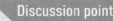

Honesty means being trustworthy and truthful. It is an important principle and value and should always be practised by all health and social care workers. Being honest in a helping situation should encourage a relaxed feeling between the carer and the user of service, and this will help create the best environment for communication to take place.

An important factor of being honest includes the willingness to admit to your mistakes so that they can be corrected. However, it is not always easy to be completely honest.

Case study

Bill is 79 and lives in a residential care home. He is used to regular visits from his grandchildren, as they call in on their way home from school. Suddenly one of the grandchildren stops visiting. The care staff have been told that the grandchild is in hospital following a serious accident, they have been asked not to tell Bill as the news will cause him much worry and distress. The carers understand the wishes of the family but feel unhappy that they are not telling Bill the truth.

How would you handle this difficult problem without damaging the relationship between Bill and the carers?

Discussion point

You have learned that empathy is not the same as sympathy.

With a partner, give examples of using sympathy and examples of using empathy.

Legislation at work

Link

This topic links to Unit 7: Equality and Diversity in Health and Social Care.

Equality Act 2010

Imagine being told that you cannot use the same entrance into school or college as your friends because you are different; or that you are not suitable for your chosen career just because you would look different from your colleagues.

In the past such **discrimination** was accepted as normal. However, over time attitudes have changed and legislation has changed, making many discriminatory practices against the law. This Act should ensure that discrimination no longer occurs.

Activity   Similarities and differences

Work in groups of four or five.

• Investigate your differences and your similarities. Think about your eye colour, religion, food preferences and music taste. You might be surprised how similar you are – and how different!

• Produce posters showing the results of your investigations.

Why is this law so important?

The **Equality** Act brings together a number of existing pieces of legislation, and significantly adds to them and strengthens them. The existing laws in the Equality Act include those covering race and disability. One of the key changes is that it adds legal protection against discrimination in these areas:

• age
• disability
• gender reassignment
• marriage and civil partnership
• pregnancy and maternity
• race
• religion or belief
• **sex**
• **gender**
• sexual orientation.

The Equality Act can be used to help protect and support the rights of individuals in all walks of life, including in health and social care settings.

Did you know?

It is illegal to discriminate against people because of their gender, sexuality, religion, ethnicity, race or age.

Activity   Equality Act 2010

In pairs, devise a presentation that illustrates how the Equality Act 2010 can benefit service users.

Care settings – as all workplaces – must do all they can to promote equality and to value difference. Codes of practice or charters should have been put in place for staff to follow and adhere to. Codes and charters will be developed from the relevant legislation, and these can be used to provide information in the form of leaflets and posters to discourage **prejudice** and encourage non-discriminatory practice.

Human Rights Act 1998

Human rights are the rights and freedoms that everyone living in the UK has, regardless of their nationality or their citizenship status.

There are 16 basic human rights laid down in the law. These rights are based on the European Convention on Human Rights, written after the Second World War. The rights include freedom of religious beliefs and freedom of speech – that is, freedom for a person to speak as they see fit.

Mental Health Act 1983

Sometimes people using services need care and treatment for mental health problems that they are not willing to accept. This may include compulsory care to protect themselves or other people. This can conflict with an individual's right to choice and independence. The Mental Health Act 1983 sets out the criteria that must be met before compulsory measures can be taken, along with protections and safeguards for patients.

Key terms

Discrimination – treating a person or group differently from others.

Equality – equal treatment and respect.

Sex – the physical and biological differences between male and female.

Gender – the social and cultural differences between male and female.

Prejudice – an unreasonable feeling against a person or group of people.

Why do you think it might be difficult for patients to accept they are mentally ill?

Individuals' rights and diversity

Diversity and equality

Equality does not mean treating everybody the same, it means giving everyone the same opportunities. Diversity is the way in which people are different. In health and social care it is necessary to promote equality by respecting diversity. For example, everyone should be able to register with a GP (equality). However, someone with more health problems will need to take up more of the doctor's time (diversity).

Just checking

Bill and Thomas live in a care home and always go in to lunch together.

The chef always gives Bill and Thomas the same size of portions.

1 Are Bill and Thomas being treated equally?

2 What steps could the care home take to encourage their workers to treat residents equally while respecting their differences?

Assessment activity 8.1

2A.P1 | 2A.P2 | 2A.M1 | 2A.D1

You work as an assistant at the Good Days Community Centre. Several different community groups use the centre for their sessions. These include a lunch club for people with dementia, a music group for young adults with learning disabilities and an exercise class for people who are recovering from heart attacks. It is part of your role to help out at these sessions and to make sure that all the people using your community centre have their rights respected. Volunteers often come and help out at the sessions and your manager has asked you to put together some materials to tell them more about the rights of service users.

Put together a pack for the volunteers. This could include a poster outlining individuals' rights when using health and social care services and telling people how the law protects rights.

It could also include a leaflet for the volunteers about how they can help to support individuals' rights and what benefits there are to everyone when they do. It could include case studies about making difficult decisions about upholding conflicting rights.

Tips

You could use someone from each of the service user groups as an example when describing individuals' rights and how to uphold them.

When you are describing a difficult decision about rights, you could describe a conflict between the rights of two different service users, or a conflict between the rights of a service user and an employee or volunteer's responsibilities.

WorkSpace

► CLAIRE DAVIES

Healthcare Assistant

I have only been working as a care assistant for four months, but already I feel that I have changed because I have learned so much from so many different people. Not only have I learned from my supervisor and the team that I work with, but also from the service users themselves – I would never have thought this!

Although each working day follows a pattern, no two days are ever the same, so I am never bored. The service users all have different personalities and characters – they really keep me on the go! My job involves supporting the qualified staff in caring for and safeguarding service users. I also work with the activities coordinator and sometimes run the activities.

One of my main responsibilities is at meal times. I ensure that service users get to the dining room, or I will take a meal to someone who does not want to eat there. I often sit with service users at meal times and chat with them so it becomes a social occasion instead of just a means of getting nourishment.

I enjoy the personal care time that I spend with people. I can assist them when they ask, sometimes by just choosing an outfit for the day or helping put on some lipstick. Other times I might read articles from the magazines or newspapers that they really enjoy.

I love my job and would never have thought going to work could be so satisfying and worthwhile. I am hoping to continue studying and to start nurse training in the future.

Think about it

1 How might Claire be supporting service users' rights during her working day?
2 Do you think that Claire has to respect confidentiality in her work?

Responsibility for safety

Introduction

Service users have rights to be independent, to be safe and to take risks. In this topic we will investigate the employer's and employee's responsibilities in the area of ensuring safety and preventing harm, both to service users and to all who might be in the health and social care setting.

Employer responsibilities

The employer in a health and social care setting has a variety of responsibilities towards their employees, service users and environment and just about everything that occurs on the premises.

Employers have a duty to ensure that they meet their responsibilities under health and safety legislation – the Health and Safety at Work Act 1974 – and must be aware of the action to take in order to safeguard both their workers and their service users.

Employers are responsible for seeing that any risks to health and safety are properly controlled. To do this, employers must provide risk assessment examples and checklists for staff training and for self-assessment.

Figure 8.2 What hazards can you see here?

Employee responsibilities

The employee also has many responsibilities, which often vary from day to day.

One of the most important responsibilities of an employee is to maximise the safety of everyone who is associated with the workplace.

As an employee your most important responsibilities are to:

- look after your own health and safety
- take care not to put other people at risk by what you do – or what you don't do – in the course of your work
- cooperate with your employer, making sure that you undertake proper training
- make sure that you understand and follow health and safety policies
- report any injuries or illnesses that you suffer as a result of doing your job
- tell your employer if something affects your ability to work, e.g. an injury or pregnancy, as your employer may need to change your duties.

Duty of care

Case study

An individual that you are caring for is pouring a cup of tea. The individual is very shaky and you are worried the tea will spill and burn him.

What do you do?

As a care worker who is aware of respecting the dignity of others, you might let the person carry on.

As a care worker who is aware of individuals maintaining their independence, you might let the person carry on.

As a care worker who is aware of the safety of individuals, you might offer to pour the tea yourself.

BUT – you want to respect dignity, help maintain independence AND keep the individual from harm, so you suggest that you work with the individual and so ensure that no harm occurs.

Care workers encourage people to live independently. That means enabling them to make decisions and take actions themselves. When someone in care decides to do something that is considered to be unsafe there is a dilemma (a difficult choice between two decisions). If we stop them doing it, are we denying them the right to take risks? If we let them do something dangerous, are we failing in our duty of care?

Care workers must know how to address dilemmas that arise between an individual's rights and the duty of care.

In the health and social care setting the service provider is a responsible person who has a **duty of care** to protect service users from harm.

Having a 'duty of care' means that the health and safety of the service user should be central to the carer's work. All treatment given must have a therapeutic benefit to the user or must be essential for saving life.

We saw earlier that employers are responsible for the health and safety of their employees while they are at work; this responsibility is covered by 'duty of care'. Employers are also responsible for any visitors to their premises such as customers, suppliers and the general public.

Key terms

Duty of care – responsibility to keep people in our care safe from harm.

Risk assessment

Introduction

We take risks and assess hazards all the time, often without thinking. For example, when we cross the road (the hazard) the risk is that we could be knocked down by a car. To ensure that we don't get knocked down we do a quick assessment of the situation – is there any traffic coming? How fast is it going? Is there a crossing nearby? Can I get to the other side safely? This is a risk assessment.

When we take risks we weigh up the options and choices that we have – for instance, should I dodge between the traffic, or wait for a gap?

Individuals vary in their ability to assess hazards and risks. Some service users need more help in weighing up the options and choices before making a decision. For example, the very young might not understand when food is 'off' – when it is likely to cause illness – and might need more help when choosing food from the fridge.

Risk management

Part of risk management involves recognising and reporting adverse events, **accidents**, **incidents**, **errors** and **near misses**. Under the Health and Safety at Work Act 1974, employees are required to report problems like these to their employer. In some circumstances they may also need to report them to the **HSE** (Health and Safety Executive).

More accidents occur in the home than anywhere else. Care workers can often prevent injury and illness through careful monitoring of potential hazards and assessment of risks.

Falls and food poisoning are major causes of hospitalisation, but with care people can be kept well and free from harm. Fridges and freezers should be clean, set to the correct temperatures and the products should be used in date order – for example, if there are two bottles of milk dated the 10th and the 12th, use up the one dated the 10th first. Always ensure that food is not consumed after its use-by date.

Risk assessment and risk management are vital for all service users and should be reviewed and updated regularly, but especially when service users receive bad news, whether it is to do with their personal life outside the care environment or their progress through the health and care system.

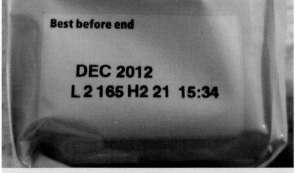

Best before end

DEC 2012
L 2 165 H2 21 15:34

Do you know the difference between 'best before' and 'use by'?

Activity   Risk assessment

The table below gives an example of a risk assessment sheet.

Concentrate on one area of your work placement setting, or a health/care setting that you have visited recently, identify hazards and fill in the rest of the table as shown in the example.

Table 8.1 Sample risk assessment

What are the hazards?	Who might be harmed and how?	What are you already doing?	Do you need to do anything else to manage this risk?	Action required by whom?	Action required by when?	Done – date
Falls	Staff and visitors could be injured if they trip over objects.	General housekeeping. All areas are well lit. There are no trailing cables.	Better housekeeping in residents' living room. Keep passages clear, put cleaning resources in cupboards when finished with.	All staff to monitor.		

Preventing harm to service users

Introduction

We all have the right to be safe and to be free from harm. All health and social care settings must have a 'health and safety' policy that sets out rules, regulations and actions that must be followed.

We have seen that there is legislation set down by government and there are policies and guidelines put in place by the work setting. All of these can help prevent harm to service users, visitors and service providers.

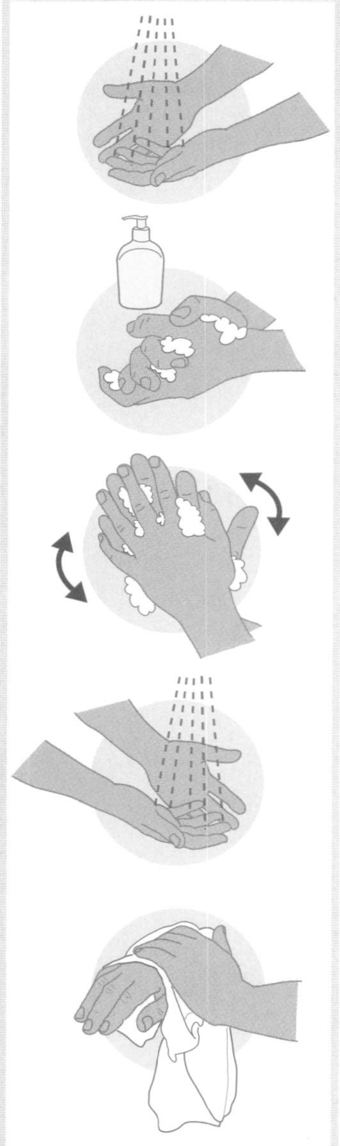

Figure 8.3 Do you always follow these steps to good hand washing?

Safeguarding

Safeguarding means protecting people's health, wellbeing and human rights, as well as enabling them to live free from harm, abuse and neglect.

In health and social care, employers and employees have a duty to safeguard the people in their care. Employers can do this by making sure that they employ the right people to work with service users, for example by doing a CRB check. They must also have good training in place for their employees, clear policies about what to do if abuse is discovered, and accessible ways for anyone to report suspected abuse. Employees need to comply with their workplace codes of conduct and report possible signs of abuse.

Other causes of harm

Harm can be caused by injury and by illness, but many injuries and illnesses can be prevented by using good risk-assessment procedures. However, this cannot cover everything that could possibly happen.

In most health and social care environments there are substances that could be harmful to the health of service users. These could include cleaning products that need to be stored correctly to avoid accidents involving trips and falls or unintended consumption. There may also be medicines stored on site. To avoid accidents such as dispensing the wrong medicine or overconsumption, medicines should be the responsibility of a trained member of staff.

If something has gone wrong in a health and social care setting, further harm, or future harm to anyone else can be prevented by having a clear complaints procedure. Employees working in health and social care need to know how their facility's complaints procedure works in order to be able to help those who need to complain and to assist in learning from previous complaints.

Enough clean toilets and washing facilities for service users and staff can help everyone to avoid infections and diseases.

The use of protective equipment – disposable gloves and aprons, for instance, should be worn when undertaking certain duties to prevent the transmission of bacteria and viruses.

However, the easiest way to prevent the spread of germs is by washing your hands.

The flu virus can also cause severe illness and death, especially in vulnerable individuals. The flu virus can live outside the body for 24–48 hours on hard surfaces; 8–12 hours on cloth, paper and tissues; and five minutes on the skin.

Service providers and service users should all be encouraged to take advantage of vaccinations – the spread of the seasonal flu virus can be greatly reduced if people take up the offer of vaccinations when offered.

Assessment activity 8.2   2B.P3 | 2B.M2 | 2B.D2

You are working in a local health and social care setting and it is part of your role to ensure that the health and safety of residents is protected. A new care assistant has just been appointed in a similar role and your manager has asked you to prepare some materials about how to maximise the safety of service users to share with the new employee.

Your materials could include:

1 An outline of the main ways you maximise health and safety for service users in your setting.

2 A completed risk assessment for a day out with a group of residents with an explanation of the importance of the risk assessment and why you have included some items on your assessment. You should also highlight where items on your risk assessment bring up conflicts between keeping service users safe and respecting their other rights.

Tips

You could relate this activity to a setting where you have done work experience, or somewhere you have done an observation visit.

You can draw your own risk assessment form based on the one shown earlier in the unit, or your teacher or tutor may supply a blank copy for you to use.

Take it further

Investigate the Management of Health and Safety at Work Regulations 1999. These cover the way previous legislation, for example the Health and Safety at Work Act 1974, should be implemented in the workplace.

How does the health and safety policy of a setting you have visited, or where you have completed a work placement, relate to the legislation?

Maintaining, storage and retrieval of information

Getting started ▶▶

Without effective communication the work of health and social care workers would soon become muddled and disjointed. The needs and rights of service users would become subject to mistakes and abuse.

Accurate recording, maintaining, storing and retrieving information is a vital part of the communication process.

How many methods of communication can you think of?

How many methods of storing information are you aware of?

▶ Recording information

There is often a need to communicate information about service users between workers. Information must be checked and recorded accurately. Incorrect recording could be dangerous and lead to mistakes in care.

Storing and retrieving information

Not so long ago all information was stored on paper in filing cabinets. Although most health and care settings still record information on paper, much is now stored electronically online. Did you know that an EPR – electronic patient record – system is in place in many GP surgeries and hospitals? This records all the information about a patient's diagnosis and treatment.

Increasingly, people can make appointments, order repeat prescriptions and leave messages for their GP on the surgery's IT system via computer, smart phone or tablet.

A service user who has been issued with their own password can access some of the information that is stored electronically about them.

In order to make sure that these electronic records are not accessed by the wrong people, it is necessary to have secure passwords and networks over which to view the information.

Now that most people carry a smart phone, they are carrying the means to store and transmit data and photographs. It is important that people working in health and social care remember not to store information about service users on insecure devices. Since many people record their activities over social networking sites, it is also important to avoid sharing information about service users in such a public way.

Confidential information should not be shared over personal phones or tablets.

Confidentiality

Confidentiality is a main principle that protects the rights of individuals. It is part of the right to privacy and the right to dignity. Workers in health and social care have a duty of confidentiality – this means that when a service user gives personal information, it is expected that the information remains confidential.

The service user should always be asked if it is all right to let other people know information about them. The exception to this is that information can be passed to others who have a right and a need to know, for example other professionals involved in that service user's ongoing care.

Information should never be passed on to those who do not need it: for instance, friends or family members of the service user.

Health and care workers should never:

- discuss matters related to service users outside the care setting
- discuss a service user with colleagues in public where they may be overheard
- leave records unattended where they may be read by unauthorised people.

Maintaining confidentiality can also be a way of safeguarding service users. A service user may have a relative who has been abusive in the past. In a situation like this, even sharing basic information about someone's contact address can put them at risk of further abuse.

Key terms

Confidential – private; not available for general discussion or publication.

Remember

Information about service users is confidential, both legally and ethically.

What should you do if family members ask you for information about a service user?

Disclosing information

Introduction

Health and social care professionals will sometimes be asked to disclose information about people using your service. Sometimes they may want or need to share confidential information that a service user has shared with them.

There are legal and ethical reasons why information belonging to service users is confidential. It should not be used in a way that might identify a service user without their informed consent.

Disclosing information to service users

Service users are entitled to see information about themselves and their care. This is covered by the **Data** Protection Act 1998 and the Freedom of Information Act 2000.

Disclosing information to others

Information should never be shared about service users without their permission, unless it is directly part of their care or necessary to prevent harm to them or others. The type of information you can share and the circumstances under which you can do so are set out in the Data Protection Act 1998.

If it appears that information needs to be passed on it is important to first ask the individual for their agreement; it is wrong to pass on even birth dates or contact details without permission. It might be possible to agree a compromise where use or sharing of information is acceptable to the service user and the quality of care isn't compromised.

◤ The Data Protection Act 1998

The Data Protection Act applies to all organisations that hold or process personal data. There are no exceptions.

The following provisions exist under the Data Protection Act 1998:

- Service users have a right to know what information is held about them and a right to access information about themselves.
- The Data Protection Act 1998 covers both paper and electronic records.
- Service users do have the right to refuse to provide information.
- Data held should be accurate and up to date; individuals have the right to correct wrong information about them.
- Data should not be kept longer than necessary.
- Information is confidential and should not be accessible to unauthorised people.
- Information must be kept secure.

Breaching a service user's confidence

Have you ever asked someone to keep a secret? Or promised that you would not tell?

Are there occasions when it is right to disclose something that has been told to you in confidence? Are there situations where it is not right to 'promise not to tell'?

Sometimes it is right and necessary to breach a confidence, despite confidentiality being an important right of individuals. An example of this is where it appears that a service user might harm themselves or others. Another example is if you know that someone is about to break, or has already broken, the law.

Activity — Breaching confidence

In groups of four or five consider the following points and decide the action that you should take. Discuss the possible advantages and disadvantages of your actions.

1 As a care worker at a training centre for young adults you are told by a service user with severe learning difficulties that she is going to have a baby. When you tell her that you must inform her key worker she bursts into tears, saying it should be kept secret.

2 Your best friend tells you that he would like to be a social care worker like you, but wants some more advice and insight. He knows that as a community care assistant you visit the Brown family on the street where he lives and he would like you to tell him all about them.

3 A nursery worker is asked by the father of one of the children for the child's address so that he can visit with a birthday present.

Assessment activity 8.3   2B.P4 | 2B.M3 | 2B.D3

You are a care worker in a residential home for older people. Following some examples in the media about breaches of confidentiality, your manager has decided that it is time to run a refresher course for all staff. As she knows you have studied this subject, she asks you to give a presentation.

The presentation should include a handout for the audience and cover the following:

1 Examples of recent breaches of confidentiality and the effect of these on the victims.

2 What the relevant laws mean for people working in health and social care, as well as the ethical reasons for maintaining confidentiality.

3 How to keep information private and confidential.

4 At least two examples of a time when you would need to breach a confidence.

Tips

This is a very tricky area and you should be aware of the implications for yourself, the service user and for your employer. Legislation does allow for breach of confidentiality in some circumstances, so you should research this to ensure you are acting in accordance with the law.

A

Abstract thinking – the ability to think about something that might not be there or even exist.

Accent – a way of pronouncing a language.

Accident – an incident, usually with negative results, that leads to harm, loss or damage to anyone in care, visitors or workers.

Adaptation – changing something, such as a service or device, so that it becomes suitable for a new situation or person.

Advocate – a person responsible for acting and speaking on behalf of someone who is unable to do so.

Agent – a person who causes a change.

Anaemia – a medical condition in which there are too few red cells in your blood.

Antibiotic – a prescribed drug that kills or prevents the growth of bacteria.

Appropriate terms – ways of addressing individuals that do not offend them.

Atonement – something done to make up for an injury or wrong.

Autonomy – freedom to make your own decisions.

B

Beliefs – strongly held opinions.

Beneficence – doing good and not harm to an individual.

Body Mass Index (BMI) – a method of determining the proportion of body fat a person has, found by dividing a person's weight measured in kg by the square of their height in metres.

Bond – to form an attachment with a parent/carer.

C

Cervix – the entrance to the uterus from the vagina.

Circumcision – male circumcision is the removal of some or all of the foreskin from the penis.

Civil liberties – people's rights and freedoms in society, such as the right to privacy.

Civil partnership – the legal equivalent of marriage between two people of the same gender.

Clarification – making something clear and understandable.

Code of practice – list of rules which state how health and social care must be delivered.

Cohabitation – where two people live together as partners but without a legal basis for their relationship, such as marriage or a civil partnership.

Cohabiting – people living together in an emotionally and/or sexually intimate relationship.

Colleague – a person you work with.

Communication – the exchange of information between people.

Confidential – information that is secret. It has been entrusted to only the person to whom it has been communicated. It is private and not open for general discussion or publication.

Context – the circumstances and setting in which an event occurs.

CPR – cardiopulmonary resuscitation, a means to resuscitate someone whose breathing or heartbeat has ceased.

Culture – the beliefs, language, styles of dress, ways of cooking, religion, ways of behaving, etc. shared by a particular group of people.

D

Data – this includes all information, whether it is facts, figures or images.

Deficiency (nutrition) – a lack of a nutrient that is necessary for wellbeing.

Dementia – an illness that affects the brain and memory, and makes you gradually lose the ability to think and behave normally.

Dental caries – the formation of dental cavities as a result of bacteria.

Deregistration – to be removed from a register, e.g. no longer allowed to run a residential care home.

Dialect – a way of speaking found only in a certain area or among a certain group or class of people.

Dignity – a calm and serious manner/style suitable for the situation and to treat someone with respect.

Disclose – making something known that was previously unknown or confidential.

Discriminate – to treat a person or group differently from others.

Diversity – variety.

Duty of care – responsibility to keep people in our care safe from harm.

Dysfunction – when the physical or emotional aspects of a relationship are not working as expected.

E

Egocentric – seeing things from only your own perspective or viewpoint.

Empathy – imaging yourself in someone else's position in order to share and understand their emotions.

Employment prospects – the ability to gain and keep a job which has a good income and the chance of promotion.

Empower – to give service users control of their own lives.

Empowerment – enabling individuals to take responsibility for their own lives by making informed decisions.

Enablement – ways and means to act independently.

Equality – equal treatment and respect.

Error – a mistake, a wrong decision or wrong action.

Eternity – an endless amount of time.

Ethical – morally right and decent; virtuous and honourable.

Ethics – a system of moral principles; the rules of conduct recognised in a group or culture.

Ethnicity – being part of a group sharing the same way of life and culture.

Evaluate – gather and review evidence, and make a judgement as to success.

F

Family – a social group made up of people who are connected or related to each other, by blood, marriage or **cohabitation**.

Fine motor skill – the ability to control and coordinate the movements of the hands and fingers, e.g. writing, painting, tying shoelaces and holding a spoon.

Formal – polite, respectful or conventional.

Fulfilment – the opportunity to accomplish personal goals and use abilities to the full.

G

Gender – the social and cultural differences between male and female.

Gender role – a role that is determined by a person's gender.

Gross motor skill – the ability to control and coordinate the movement of the large limbs of the body, e.g. crawling, walking and running.

H

Hazard – a situation or object that could cause damage or hurt.

Hierarchy – a list or diagram of things or people arranged in order of importance, with each level considered superior to the level below.

High biological value protein – a protein that provides the body with all eight essential amino acids.

HSE – Health and Safety Executive, the body that regulates health and safety in the workplace.

I

Immunisation – to make someone immune to a disease, usually by vaccination.

Incident – anything unusual that happens to individuals in care, visitors or workers.

Income – the amount of money people receive from their work, savings, pension or welfare benefits.

Independence – freedom from control by, or dependence on, others.

Informal – casual.

Infringing – going too far, or overstepping the mark.

J

Jargon – technical words used by a professional person as a short way of saying things. These can be hard for non-professionals to understand.

Judgemental – making decisions or forming opinions on the basis of something such as appearance, without proper evidence, and being too critical.

K

Kosher – food that satisfies the requirements of Jewish law; for example, when an animal is slaughtered, all the blood must be drained from its body before it can be eaten.

L

Language development – the process which children go through as they learn to communicate with others using words and speech.

Legal requirement – something that has to be done by law.

Life expectancy – the average number of years a person can expect to live from birth.

Life stages – a number of distinct phases people pass through during their lives.

Line manager – the person who is in charge of your department, group or project at work.

Literacy skills – abilities required to speak, read and write clearly, correctly and accurately.

Litigation – the act or process of bringing or contesting a legal action in court.

M

Malnutrition – lack of proper nutrition, caused by not having enough to eat, not eating enough of the right things, or being unable to use the food that one does eat.

Manual work – work that requires the use of physical skills.

Material possessions – objects which can be bought, but are non-essential to live, e.g. designer clothing.

Menopause – the natural and permanent stopping of menstruation (periods), occurring usually between the ages of 45 and 55.

Mid-life crisis – a dramatic period of self-doubt caused by the passing of youth and the move into later adulthood.

N

Nation – a large community of people who share a common language, culture, ethnicity, descent, and/or history and usually a territory. In this unit 'nation' refers to the United Kingdom (UK).

Near miss – an event that could have caused harm, loss or damage, but did not.

Non-manual work – work that depends primarily on mental skills.

O

Obese – having a body mass index (BMI) of 30 or more.

Oestrogen – a hormone produced in a women's ovaries that controls the development of sexual characteristics and stimulates changes in the reproductive organs.

Offence – words that cause offence can include racist terms or terms that insult an individual's gender, disability or sexuality.

Osteoporosis – a medical condition in which your bones become weak and break easily.

P

Pathogen – a microorganism that causes disease, such as bacteria and viruses.

Parallel play – children play alongside each other, but not together.

Peer group – the social group a person belongs to which influences beliefs and behaviour.

Personal space – the area immediately surrounding a person that they consider to be their own personal territory. People generally feel uncomfortable if others 'invade' this personal space. Everyone's idea of personal space is different.

Person-centred approach – working with individuals to identify their values, needs and expectations.

PIES – four groups of human growth and development: Physical, Intellectual, Emotional and Social.

Plaque – a harmful substance which forms on your teeth, which bacteria can live and breed in.

Poverty – having insufficient money to afford the essentials to live.

Prejudice – an unreasonable feeling against a person or group or people.

Proactive – creating or controlling a situation by causing something to happen rather than responding after something has happened.

Professional bodies – organisations that set standards for, and look after the interests of, their members, e.g. the Royal College of Nursing.

Proximity – the distance between someone or something.

Q

Questionnaire – a list of questions in writing, designed to gather information on a specific subject.

R

Religion – a set of beliefs based on the idea of a sacred being.

Respect – showing recognition of the value of an individual.

Rights – things that a person can claim they are free to do or that are due to them.

Risk assessment – investigating all hazards and offering precautions to prevent harm.

Role model – someone whose behaviour and/or attitudes people try to copy because they admire them.

S

Safeguarding – a precautionary measure to prevent injury or abuse.

Screening – mass checking of sectors of the population for early signs of a particular disease or condition.

Secular – something that has no connection to any religion or place of worship.

Self-esteem – how much you like, accept and respect yourself as a person, how you value yourself.

Self image – the mental picture we have of ourselves.

Sex – the physical and biological differences between male and female.

Slang – the use of informal words and expressions that are not considered standard in the speaker's dialect or language.

Social class – a group of people who share a common place in society.

Social development – the ability to interact with others in society and build relationships.

Social isolation – when people live without regular contact with other people, especially family and friends.

Social play – children play together, sharing their toys.

Solitary play – children play alone using their imagination and do not interact with other children.

Statistics – the collection, organisation and interpretation of numerical data. In health and social care, statistics could include things like the numbers of people suffering from particular conditions and the incidence of accidents.

Statutory – set up and regulated by the government (according to statute or law).

Stereotype – a fixed idea about an individual or group of people.

Stereotyping – thinking a group of people will all have the same attribute, for example, that all older people are deaf and forgetful.

Superbug – a bacterial infection that is resistant to almost all antibiotics.

Survey – a broad investigation of a subject, often informed by asking questions of a representative group.

Sympathy – feeling pity or sorrow for another person's feelings, emotions or distress.

T

Testosterone – a hormone produced by the testes that controls the development of male sexual characteristics.

Tolerance – the capacity to recognise and respect the beliefs or practices of others, even if we don't agree with them.

U

Underpin – to provide a supporting framework.

V

Vaccination – the introduction of a very small quantity of a weakened form of a disease into the body, usually by injection, to help the body develop antibodies to that particular disease.

Values – the ideas that lie behind and inform good health and social care practice.

Vulnerable – open to being hurt emotionally or physically.

W

Wealth – riches, lots of goods and money.

Weaning – introduction of solid food into the baby's diet from about six months of age.

Index